CAMBRIDGE MONOGRAPHS IN
EXPERIMENTAL BIOLOGY
No. 10

EDITORS:
M. ABERCROMBIE, P. B. MEDAWAR,
GEORGE SALT (*General Editor*)
M. M. SWANN, V. B. WIGGLESWORTH

ENDOCRINE CONTROL
IN
CRUSTACEANS

THE SERIES

ENDOCRINE CONTROL IN CRUSTACEANS

BY

DAVID B. CARLISLE

Endocrinologist, Plymouth Laboratory,
Marine Biological Association of the United Kingdom

AND

SIR FRANCIS KNOWLES, BART

Head of the Biology Department, Marlborough College

CAMBRIDGE
AT THE UNIVERSITY PRESS
1959

PUBLISHED BY
THE SYNDICS OF THE CAMBRIDGE UNIVERSITY PRESS

Bentley House, 200 Euston Road, London, N.W. 1
American Branch: 32 East 57th Street, New York 22, N.Y.

©

CAMBRIDGE UNIVERSITY PRESS

1959

Printed in Great Britain at the University Press, Cambridge
(Brooke Crutchley, University Printer)

CONTENTS

LIST OF PLATES

AUTHORS' NOTE

EACH of us, while accepting a general responsibility for the whole, is primarily responsible for a different section of this book. Each has contributed that portion which deals with subjects in which he has had most experience and has contributed original observations. Thus Chapters 1, 2 and 3 are the work of Sir Francis Knowles and Chapters 4, 5, 6 and 7 are the work of Dr David Carlisle, though each section has been modified in the light of the other author's criticisms. Consequently any theories put forward may be personal ones, though for the sake of simplicity we have used the first person plural throughout.

One of us (F.G.W.K.) has incorporated in this book many of the results obtained during research work which was supported by a grant from the Nuffield Foundation, and he would like to take this opportunity of acknowledging this aid. We should also like to thank the numerous individuals who have afforded critical help in preparing this book, especially Dr F. S. Russell, F.R.S., and Dr P. Karlson. Finally, we are grateful to the editor and publishers of *Endeavour* for the loan of blocks for the colour plates.

CHAPTER I

Introduction

DURING the past twenty years a number of reviews have marked the progress of our understanding of endocrine control in crustaceans. Some of these reviews have dealt exclusively with crustacean endocrinology (e.g. Kleinholz, 1942; Brown, 1944; Panouse, 1947; Brown, 1952; Knowles and Carlisle, 1956). Other reviews have considered crustacean hormones in a general survey of invertebrate endocrines (e.g. Koller, 1929, 1938; Hanström, 1939; Lerma, 1936; Scharrer, 1954, 1955; Gabe, 1954; etc.). It is not the intention of this book to present yet another comprehensive survey of the literature but rather to select studies which mark significant advances in our knowledge of endocrine control in crustaceans. We hope that by so illustrating the changing trends of research in crustacean endocrinology since its inception until the present day we may present the pattern of our knowledge in relation to the past discoveries on which it is based and may predict possible future trends.

The study of crustacean endocrines began in 1928 with the independent discoveries by Perkins, working on the prawn *Palaemonetes*, and Koller, who studied the shrimp *Crangon*, that the colour changes of crustaceans were controlled by chemical substances circulating in the blood stream. These conclusions were based on experiments involving an interference with the blood flow or injections of extracts. Both authors found that extracts of the eyestalks when injected into dark animals resulted in an intense and prolonged paling due to concentration of pigment within the chromatophores. During the first decade following this discovery of the hormonal control of colour change in crustaceans investigators directed their attention mainly to the following problems:

(1) Localization and identification of the organ in the eyestalk responsible for the production of the body-lightening hormone.

(2) A more intensive study of the chromatophores of crustaceans and the factors influencing them.

The name of Professor Hanström will always be associated with the discovery of the first known endocrine organ in crustaceans, namely the sinus gland. He and his pupils in a series of researches carried out from 1931 to 1937 showed that there were two structures in the crustacean eyestalk which both on histological and physiological grounds could be suspected of hormone secretion. Their experiments were based on the extraction of different sections of eyestalks of various crustaceans and the effects of these extracts on the chromatophore system. A definite correlation was found between the presence of the sinus gland and the abundance of a chromactivating substance; a correspondence between the X organ and colour change was less definite, though there did seem to be some relationship.

During the 1930's Kleinholz added the distal and reflecting retinal pigments to the other pigment movements shown to be under hormonal control. He found that injections of eyestalk extracts into animals in darkness brought about a typical light-adaptation of the eye. In the field of colour change investigation was mainly directed on the number of hormones which might be implicated in the very diverse movements of pigments within the chromatophores. Brown (1935 a, b) observed that the four pigments found within the chromatophores of *Palaemonetes* showed independent behaviour in the responses to various backgrounds and concluded that at least four hormones must be operating to account for this independence. On the other hand, Abramowitz (1937 b) carried out a number of reciprocal injection experiments between different species and concluded that there was but a single pigment-activating hormone and that the evident independent movements of the pigments might be explicable in terms of specific differences of the end organs. He made attempts to clarify the problem by chemical analysis of the colour change hormone extracted from the eyestalks of the crab *Uca*, but he was unable to obtain a sufficient amount of material to enable him to reach any definite conclusions. The material which he was studying brought about, when injected, a darkening of eyestalkless *Uca*. Carlson (1935) had drawn attention to this difference between the effects of eyestalk extracts on chromatophores in crustaceans; an eyestalk extract which paled *Palaemonetes* appeared to darken *Uca*, and vice versa. Clearly these results could be explained either by a 'unitary hormone hypothesis' in terms of differences of chromatophore response, or by a 'multiple hormone hypothesis' if it could be shown that all the crustacean eyestalks investigated contained two substances, one a *Palaemonetes*-lightening substance and the other a *Uca*-darkening substance. The arguments for and against these two hypotheses were summarized by Kleinholz (1942) in his review.

During the 1930's observers who removed the eyestalks from crustaceans noted that ecdysis was affected. A number of investigators reported that the intermoult period was shortened and that there appeared to be less calcium in the moulted exoskeleton. The evidence, however, was held by Kleinholz to be inconclusive, and in his review of the first decade of crustacean endocrinology he came to the conclusion that pigment movements were the only functions in crustaceans that were indubitably under hormonal control. His review marks the end of the first phase of crustacean endocrinology, namely the discovery that the pigment movements within chromatophores and in the eyes of crustaceans were under hormonal control, and the localization of the sinus gland and the X organ as potent sources of pigment-activating substances.

It is interesting to compare the reviews by Kleinholz (1942) and Brown (1944). Although these two publications are only separated by a few years, they differ in certain important respects, of which perhaps the most significant (in view of subsequent advances) is the emphasis laid by Brown on the evidence for the presence of chromactivating substances in the central nervous system. Perkins (1928) had found no influence of extracts of the central nervous system on *Palaemonetes* red pigment, but Brown (1933) repeated this experiment and reported that a pigment-concentrating substance was in fact present in the central nervous system. His results were criticized on the grounds that in extracting the nervous system he might have included material present in the blood stream, and that this material might have originated in the eyestalks. A few years later, however, it was shown (Knowles, 1939) that extracts of the nervous systems of crustaceans whose eyestalks had been removed three to four weeks previously had an activity upon the light-reflecting white chromatophores; this clearly could not be attributed to sinus-gland activity. The nervous system of the thorax was indicated as an especially potent source of a chromactivating substance, and in 1940 Brown and Ederstrom extended these observations by showing through injection experiments on *Crangon* that the most effective extracts of this region could be prepared from the post-oesophageal trito-cerebral commissure. Later (1946) Brown attempted to localize the source of the chromactivating substance in the commissure and reported that the greatest activity was found along the median faces of the circumoesophageal connectives and in the commissure itself; he reported that there was a concentration of chromactivators in that part of the commissure in which two slight swellings could be seen and in which a bluish green particulate substance and some cell bodies could be observed if a freshly dissected commissure was examined in sea water. He did not, however, pursue these investigations further, although he had a few years before written in his review that 'histological search of the nervous system for secretory elements is much needed'.

It is interesting to note the contrast between the evolution of crustacean and vertebrate endocrinology. The endocrine organs of the vertebrates were described in considerable detail long before experiments on their function were performed, and so in the early physiological experiments on vertebrate endocrines the selective ablation of an organ suspected of endocrine activity was comparatively easy. Crustacean endocrinology, on the other hand, was founded on simple physiological experiments, and the evidence for blood-borne hormones preceded histo-logical studies of their probable sources by many years. In short, vertebrate endocrinology was founded on anatomy but crustacean endocrinology was founded on physiology, and it is interesting to observe that the physiological approach continued for many years in the development of crustacean endocrinology. Thus, although by 1947 Hanström and Panouse were each able to present fairly comprehensive surveys of the form and gross anatomy of the sinus gland in crustaceans, there was little evidence then concerning the microscopic anatomy of secretory cellular elements either in the sinus gland or any other crus-tacean endocrine organ.

The second decade of crustacean endocrinology included a considerable number of physiological experiments based on ablation and the injection of extracts. As a result of these methods Brown and his collaborators were able to bring forward

4

evidence that the crustacean nervous system and sinus glands contained a number of distinct chromactivating substances and that the 'unitary hormone hypothesis' must be abandoned. Brown and Scudamore (1940) succeeded in separating two different active principles from the eyestalks or sinus glands of several different species of Decapoda by extracting them with 100 % ethyl alchohol and then with sea water. In every species the alcohol-soluble fraction had a relatively strong effect upon the red pigment of *Palaemonetes* and a very weak effect upon the black pigment of *Uca*. The residue after alcohol treatment had a very strong effect upon the latter, but a weaker effect upon the red pigment of *Palaemonetes*. In 1940 Brown and Ederstrom showed that, in addition to the *Palaemonetes*-lightening hormone and the *Uca*-darkening hormone, a third hormone which dispersed the dark pigments in the chromatophores of the telson and uropods could be extracted from the post-oesophageal commissure region of *Crangon*. This tail-darkening hormone could be separated from the *Palaemonetes*-lightening hormone because of its relative insolubility in alcohol. It seemed clear that the postulation of at least three hormones was necessary to explain the control of the movements of dark pigments within crustacean chromatophores, and injection experiments had also indicated the possibility of a separate hormone controlling the white pigments of the light-reflecting chromatophores (Knowles, 1939).

During the 1940's a number of investigators studied the effect of eyestalk removal on the frequency of moulting. Undoubtedly the removal of the eyestalks stimulated precocious moulting (Brown and Cunningham, 1939; Abramowitz and Abramowitz, 1939, 1940; Kleinholz and Bourquin, 1941; etc.), but the effects of eyestalk removal did not seem to be the same at all stages of the moult-cycle. Drach (1944), working on *Leander serratus*, found that removal of the eyestalks was only effective in precipitating the moult if the operation was performed during the inter-moult period, and that it had no significant effect if performed during the main period of pre-moult. The problem of the control of moult was further complicated by the observations of Scudamore (1947) who supplied evidence that the central nervous system of the crayfish contained a moult-accelerating principle. Pyle (1943) showed that the staining reaction of the sinus gland altered at the time of moult and

5

concluded that the sinus gland released substances concerned in the moult-cycle.

Two further instances of suspected hormonal control were discovered during the second decade of crustacean endocrinology, namely a possible gonad-controlling principle and a diabetogenic principle. Removal of the eyestalks in immature female crustaceans or in mature females at a time when the animals were not breeding resulted in a rapid increase in the size of the ovary (Panouse, 1943, 1944, 1946, 1947; Brown and Jones, 1949).

During an investigation of endocrine influence on carbohydrate metabolism in crustaceans Abramowitz, Hisaw and Papandrea (1944) detected that injection of extracts of the eyestalks of crabs into crabs of the genus *Callinectes* produced a pronounced increase in the amount of blood sugar, and that the greater part of the activity of the eyestalks resided in the sinus gland. On the other hand, neither they nor Kleinholz and Little (1948, 1949) could detect hypoglycaemia after ablation of the eyestalks or sinus gland removal. It had previously been reported that stress of various kinds led to hyperglycaemia in crustaceans. For example, handling, asphyxiation, the injection of brine and other forms of injury all produced forms of hyperglycaemia. If the sinus glands were removed or the nerves leading to them were cut, however (Kleinholz and Little, 1949; Kleinholz, Havel and Reichart, 1950), asphyxia no longer caused hyperglycaemia, and it seemed likely that the effects of stress were mediated through the sinus gland. In this connexion it is interesting to note that some evidence for a heart-accelerating hormone was brought forward during the second phase of crustacean endocrinology. Welsh (1937) showed that eyestalk extracts accelerated the rate of heart beat, and Scudamore (1941) found that extracts of the sinus glands alone also had this effect; he observed, however, that a heart-accelerating effect could also be obtained from extracts of the nerve cord, so arousing the suspicion that the heart-accelerating activity of eyestalk extracts might be explicable in terms of a heart-accelerating effect of nervous tissue as a whole.

We have found that the second phase of crustacean endocrinology (1940–50) was marked by three main advances: (*a*) the discovery that various aspects of metabolism, growth and development were probably under hormonal control, (*b*) evi-

6

dence that a number of different hormones were involved in the pigment movements of crustaceans, (c) suggestive evidence that chromactivating substances were produced in the central nervous system. These advances were all founded on the physiological approach, namely on experiments of ablation and the injection of extracts. The detailed structure of the secretory tissues was still incompletely known.

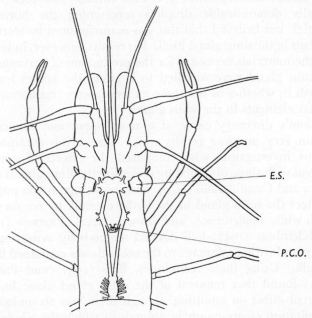

Fig. 1. The position of the principal neurosecretory release centres in crustaceans. *E.S.* Eyestalk, which contains the sinus gland and other neurosecretory systems. *P.C.O.* Post-commissure organs.

The third phase of crustacean endocrinology began in the year 1951. In that year, for the first time, the distribution of chromactivating hormones was identified with secretory droplets lying along the course of nerves leading to blood sinuses. The first direct proof of neurosecretion in crustaceans was offered by Knowles (1951) who showed that the greatest chromactivating potency in the post-oesophageal commissure region lay not in the commissure itself as had previously been suspected by Brown and his collaborators, but in two lamellae which lay adjacent to, and attached to, blood sinuses. Secretory

7

droplets could be detected in these lamellae and along the course of two fine nerves leading to these lamellae from the commissure. A few months later Enami (1951 *a*, *b*), in a very detailed survey of the presence of chromactivating substances and secretory elements in the crab *Sesarma*, showed that secretory droplets could be detected along the course of the nerves leading from a cluster of cell bodies in the medulla terminalis to the sinus gland. Enami, however, did not consider that these histologically demonstrable droplets represented the hormonal material, but believed that this was manufactured by secretory elements in the sinus gland itself. His results, however, indicated that the materials necessary for the production of hormones by the sinus gland were supplied to it along the nerves leading towards it, whether or not these materials were transformed by cellular elements in the sinus gland.

Enami's discovery came at a most opportune moment to explain very puzzling results which were being obtained by various investigators who compared the effects of eyestalk removal with those obtained by removing the sinus glands only. Brown and Cunningham (1939) had shown that it was possible to detect the sinus gland in the living eyestalk by reason of its bluish white opalescence, and Brown (1942), Panouse (1946) and Kleinholz (1947) had devised methods for removing the sinus gland without damage to the other tissues contained in the eyestalk. Using these techniques, Bliss (1951) and Passano (1951) found that removal of the sinus gland alone had no apparent effect on moulting, though there was an undoubted precipitation of pre-moult in animals in which the whole eyestalk had been removed. Clearly these results could be explained by the hypothesis that the sinus gland contained a moult-inhibiting hormone, but that the major source of production of this hormone lay not in the sinus gland but elsewhere. This problem was finally resolved by Passano (1953) who found that the effects of bilateral eyestalk ablation could be duplicated by removal of the sinus glands together with the nerve supplying them, including the cell bodies of these neurones located in the medulla terminalis. Conversely, implantation of the sinus glands and the associated neurones completely inhibited precocious moulting in animals from which the eyestalks had previously been removed. His experiments indicated that a moult-inhibiting hormone is produced in the neurones leading to the

8

PLATE I

 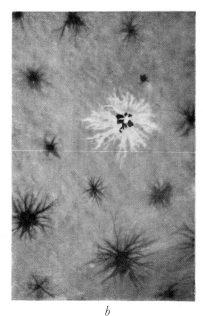

a   b

(a) Dorsal view of the cephalothorax of the prawn *Leander serratus* (× 4).
(b) A small portion of (a) highly magnified. Large red, small red and white chromatophores are shown (× 50).

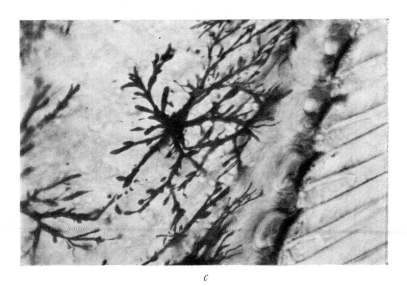

c

(c) A uropod chromatophore in which concentration of the pigment has
recently begun. The pigment has withdrawn from the finer chromorhizae, which
are therefore no longer visible (× 200).

sinus gland and that the sinus gland might be no more than a reservoir of the hormone. These results were supported by observations on the control of oxygen consumption in crabs. Removal of the sinus glands alone had little or no effect on the level of oxygen consumption or the respiratory quotient in either crabs or crayfish, but eyestalk ablation resulted in an increase of oxygen consumption (Bliss, 1951, 1953). Bliss interpreted her data as implying that a hormone controlling oxygen consumption was formed in some tissues in the eyestalk other than the sinus gland, but was stored and released at the sinus gland. It has subsequently been shown that the sinus gland is the meeting place of neurosecretory fibres from many cell groups which lie in the eyestalk and elsewhere (Bliss and Welsh, 1952; Bliss, Durand and Welsh, 1954; Carlisle, 1953a, b; Potter, 1954; Knowles, 1955). All these authors agree that the material which is produced in the neurosecretory cell bodies is transported along axon fibres, and that these fibres end in the sinus gland in the form of club-shaped terminations. Whether or not the substances brought to the sinus gland are transformed there by cellular elements is still a matter for discussion, and the evidence for and against this view will be considered later. It has become clear, however, during the past decade that most of the known crustacean hormones originate in cellular elements of the central nervous system and that the greater part of the endocrine activity in crustaceans is comparable to the neurosecretion attributed by the Scharrers and others (1954) to the hypothalamus-hypophysial system in vertebrates and the brain-corpus cardiacum system in the insects.

Although most of the endocrine effects so far demonstrated seem to be associated with neurosecretory systems, there are some which are not. Charniaux-Cotton (1954a, b) has described an endocrine gland in an amphipod which seems to be responsible for the differentiation of the primary and secondary male characteristics. Gabe (1953b) described an organ which he called the Y organ, which has been shown to affect sexual development, moulting and development of the regeneration buds of extirpated legs (Echalier, 1955).

Within recent years studies have indicated that a number of metabolic processes in crustaceans are influenced by blood-borne hormones. In addition to the moult-inhibiting substance, the ovary-inhibiting hormone and the diabetogenic principle

9

there seems to be evidence that an endocrine system is implicated also in the control of chitin formation, the decomposition of lipoids and carotenoids, the rate of oxygen consumption, calcium metabolism, water balance, testicular growth, the development of the male secondary sexual characteristics, and that moulting may be controlled by three or more different hormones, acting at different stages in the moult cycle.

Recently, and at present, a number of attempts have been made to determine the chemical nature of some of the crustacean hormones. It has been shown by means of paper electrophoresis and dialysis experiments that a number of chromactivating substances may be isolated from extracts of sinus glands and post-commissure organs (Knowles, Carlisle and Dupont-Raabe, 1955). Using chemical methods of purification Östlund and Fänge (1956) have isolated a chromactivating substance from the eyestalks of *Pandalus*. All these authors have shown that it is possible to inactivate the purified chromactivating substances by using enzymes which attack peptide linkages, and there seems to be good ground for believing that a number of the crustacean chromactivating substances are peptide in nature.

At the present moment we seem to be nearing the end of the third phase of crustacean endocrinology. During the first phase (1928–38) the presence of chromactivating hormones was demonstrated by injection and ablation experiments, and the sinus gland was indicated as a possible source of these substances. During the second phase (1939–51) extraction and injection experiments indicated that more than one hormone was implicated in the control of pigment movements, and that, in addition to the sinus gland, the central nervous system seemed to contain considerable amounts of chromactivating substances. Moreover, it was shown during this second phase that in addition to pigment movements certain metabolic activities (e.g. moulting, carbohydrate metabolism and ovarian development) should be added to the list of activities under hormonal control. The third phase began in 1951 when it was shown that most of the known endocrine systems in crustaceans were neurosecretory systems and the hormones were produced in modified neurones and transported along their axon fibres to the blood stream. It has been shown that these neurosecretory systems are complex in form and that the hormones produced by them may be numerous and affect various aspects of metabolism in addition to pigment movements and the regulation of heart beat. Some at least of these hormones seem to be peptide in nature. In this third phase of research crustacean endocrinology has approached more closely vertebrate endocrinology than hitherto, for within recent years research has shown that the vertebrate brain contains many neurosecretory pathways, most of which culminate in the neurohypophysis, and that some of the hormones released there are peptide in nature. Undoubtedly there are many differences in detail between the neurosecretory systems of arthropods and vertebrates, but there are also broad resemblances which may be shown by future research to represent certain fundamental features of the neurosecretory process, e.g. neurosecretory control of pigment movements, water balance, the peptide nature of certain products of neurosecretion, similar tinctorial affinities of a number of neurosecretory products, etc. What the significance of these resemblances may be, is still obscure and it seems to us most likely that an answer to some of the problems of neurosecretion may be found in a study of the biochemistry of the neurosecretory products and the electron microscopy of the neurosecretory tissues. At present there is only one indisputable feature which the great majority of neurosecretory systems in animals have in common, namely that the axons containing endocrine material do not innervate in a typical manner any end-organ, but terminate in, or in close contact with, the blood stream. It has been suggested that this feature may serve as an important criterion for determining whether a neurone is part of an endocrine system or not (Knowles, 1954). It is to be hoped that the next decade of crustacean endocrinology will, in addition to advancing our knowledge of endocrine control in crustaceans, reveal fundamental features of neurosecretion.

A NOTE ON NOMENCLATURE

WE have previously used the terms energetic hormones and metabolic hormones to distinguish those which have a short-term effect, quickly acting, from those whose influence is long acting over many days, producing alterations in the metabolism, growth or sexual organs (Knowles and Carlisle, 1956). This classification has certain limitations, for hormones which affect the metabolic rate are obviously altering the energy relations of the body and so in this monograph we propose utilizing a classification of hormones which has been drawn up in discussion with Dr P. M. Jenkins and which will be used also in her forthcoming book on comparative endocrinology. That category which we have formerly termed energetic hormones will here be called kinetic hormones.

Kinetic hormones are hormones which act immediately upon effector organs such as muscles, chromatophores or other endocrine glands. Among the tropic hormones we may distinguish as a sub-category the *endocrinokinetic hormones* which cause other endocrine glands to secrete or release hormones.

Metabolic hormones are hormones which produce effects upon the metabolism, by acting upon the blood sugar, calcium metabolism, water metabolism, rate of oxygen consumption, respiratory quotient or other metabolic processes.

Morphogenetic hormones are hormones which act upon sequences of growth, differentiation and maturation of the whole body or specific organ systems.

It seems possible, so far as our knowledge goes at present, that one hormone may possibly fall into more than one category. Thus calcium metabolism may be affected at the same time as moulting—perhaps a metabolic and a morphogenetic effect produced by one hormone.

CHAPTER 2

The Neurosecretory System of the Head and Thorax

DURING the past decade many investigators have brought forward histological and physiological evidence that hormones are produced in cells of the crustacean central nervous system and are transported along axon fibres to points of release into the blood stream. Thus far three main areas of release have been discovered, namely the sinus glands, the post-commissure organs and the pericardial organs. The sinus glands are located in the eyestalks of those crustaceans which have stalked eyes and in the head of those that do not; the post-commissure organs are situated immediately posterior to the oesophagus; the pericardial organs are more variable in position, but are found always in the wall of the pericardium. Each of these release centres is the meeting place of many fibres which originate elsewhere. Most of the fibres supplying the sinus glands and post-commissure organs originate in the brain, while those running to the pericardial organs seem to originate in the ventral nerve cord. The positions of the sinus glands and the post-commissure organs in *Leander* are shown at fig. 1; the pericardial organs are described in a subsequent chapter (p. 70). In this account the sinus glands and post-commissure organs will first be described, followed by a consideration of the cell bodies of the neurones which supply these centres.

THE SINUS GLAND

In 1930 Koller searched for the source of pigment-activating hormones in crustaceans, and found that a very potent extract could be obtained from tissues located near the basement membrane of the eye where he found a group of cells which he called the blood gland. Later, in a series of studies on the nervous system, Hanström (1931–4) described two structures in the crustacean eyestalk which he thought might be secretory in function; one of these was the blood gland, and the other was named the X organ. The relation between these secretory tissues and chromactivating hormones was confirmed by later localization experiments (Sjögren, 1934; Carlson, 1935, 1936; Hanström, 1937a, b; Brown, 1940, and others). Carlson (1935) carried out his experiments on the long slender eyestalks of the fiddler crab, *Uca pugilator*, and remarked that the middle third of the eyestalk contained the blood gland whereas the X organ was either very small or absent. On the other hand, Ståhl (1938a, b) found that an injection of extracts of the heads of *Diastylis*, a Cumacean, into *Leander adspersus* brought about a concentration of pigments in the chromatophores, though an examination of the tissues extracted revealed no blood gland but an apparently typical X organ. As Kleinholz (1942) remarked, these early experiments indicated that either the blood gland or the X organ, or both, might be concerned in the regulation of pigment movements within chromatophores. It was shown, however, that the blood gland was the more likely release centre as it lay in the wall of a blood sinus, and was thereby well placed for the release of hormones into the blood stream. This gland was therefore renamed the sinus gland, a name which has been retained.

The most primitive form of the sinus gland so far detected consists of a thickened disc-shaped portion of the epineurium enclosing the ganglia of the eyestalk: this condition has been described in the Mysidacea (*Eucopia*) and in the Euphausiacea (*Meganyctiphanes*). In the Decapoda, order Palaemonoidea (*Palaemonetes, Crangon, Leander, Systelaspis*) and in *Lysmata*, the sinus gland is more or less beaker-shaped (fig. 2 B) and surrounds

Fig. 2. Example of an eyestalk in which the sensory pore is fully developed—the natantian, *Lysmata seticaudata*. A. Anterior diagrammatic view of a dissection of a left eyestalk, showing the main nervous and endocrine structures. B. Longitudinal section of the sinus gland and adjacent tissues; note the nerve endings vertical to the surface of the blood sinus, and the lack of any other apparent cellular elements in the organ—a situation common, but not invariable in this species. C. A single neurosecretory cell from the ganglionic X organ (fixed: Helly's fluid; stained: Heidenhain's haematoxylin). *B.S.*, blood sinus; *B.S.G.T.*, brain-sinus gland tract; *B.T.*, brain-X organ tract; *B.V.*, blood vessel from the internal sinus of the ganglionic chain to the external blood sinus of the eyestalk; *L.G.*, lamina ganglionaris; *M.E.*, medulla externa; *M.I.*, medulla interna; *M.T.*, medulla terminalis (sometimes called lobus terminalis of the protocerebrum); *M.T.G.X.*, medulla terminalis ganglionic X organ; *P.Lo*, peduncle of the optic lobe; *S.G.*, sinus gland; *S.G.T.*, combined sinus gland tract; *S.N.*, sensory nerve; *S.P.*, sensory pore; *S.P.X.*, sensory pore X organ; *X.O.C.*, X organ connective; *X.S.G.T.*, X organ-sinus gland tract. (A and B redrawn from Carlisle, 1953e.)

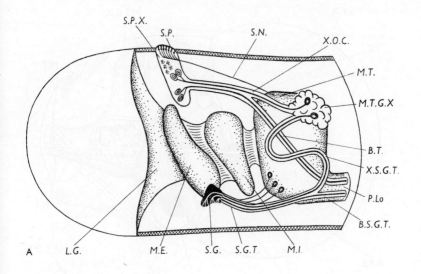

A

S.P.X. S.P. S.N. X.O.C. M.T. M.T.G.X B.T. X.S.G.T. P.Lo B.S.G.T.

L.G. M.E. S.G. S.G.T M.I.

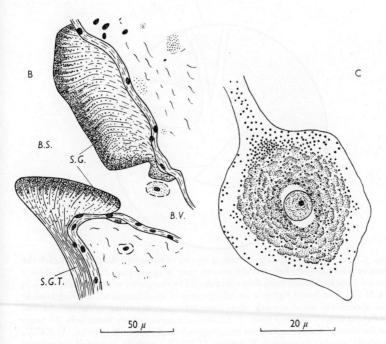

B

B.S. S.G. B.V. S.G.T.

C

50 μ   20 μ

Fig. 2. For legend see facing page.

15

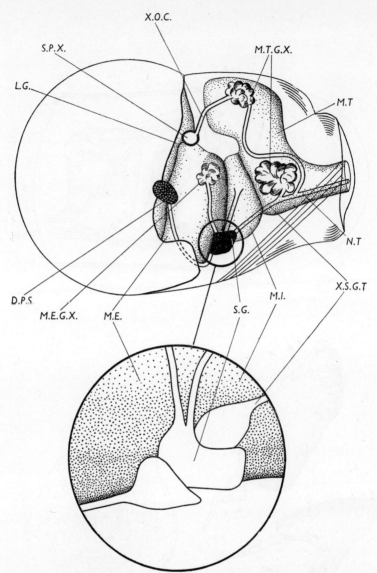

Fig. 3. The eyestalk of *Leander serratus*, a species of natantian decapod in which the sensory pore has been lost, but the sensory pore X organ (*S.P.X.*) retained. This is the left eyestalk viewed from above and should be compared with the photograph in Pl. II (*b*). The lower figure is an enlargement of the sinus gland, showing how, in this species, the gland is made up of three lobes corresponding to the innervation. *D.P.S.*, accessory pigment spot; *N.T.*, tract of neurosecretory fibres from the brain to the sinus gland; *L.G.*, lamina ganglionaris; *M.E.*, medulla externa; *M.E.G.X.*, medulla externa ganglionic X organ; *M.T.G.X.*, medulla terminalis ganglionic X organ; *M.I.*, medulla interna; *S.G.*, sinus gland; *X.S.G.T.*, X organ-sinus gland tract; *S.P.X.*, sensory pore X organ; *X.O.C.*, X organ connective.

PLATE II

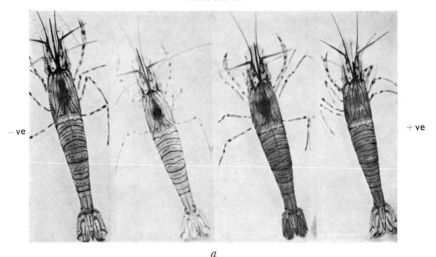

a

(*a*) Electrophoretic separation of chromactivating substances from extract of post-commissure organs (0·3 mA/cm., 16 hours, pH 7·5, 320–350 V).

A pigment-concentrating substance (A-substance) moved 2–3 cm. towards the cathode. A pigment-dispersing substance (B-substance) was displaced lightly towards the anode. Animals injected with extracts from either side of these regions were unaffected (see fig. 11).

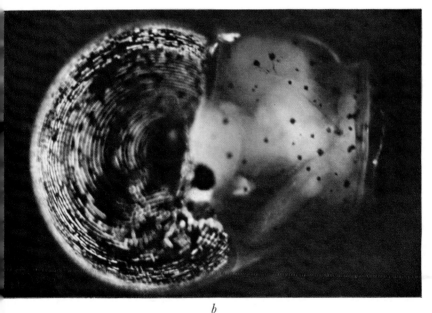

b

(*b*) The left eye and eyestalk of *Leander serratus* viewed from above a few minutes after it had been detached from the animal. For identification of the visible structures see fig. 3. There is some evidence that the disposition and form of the nervous and the neurosecretory structures of the eyestalk differ slightly in the Mediterranean and British forms of the species; this individual was taken at Naples (× 30).

the opening of a small dorso-lateral blood sinus into a large outer blood sinus in the region between the medulla interna and the medulla externa. In the Reptantia Astacura the sinus gland is more diffuse, partly extending into the large outer sinus and partly spreading over branched portions of the inner sinus (fig. 5). In the crabs the gland is slightly less diffuse, extending over the proximal portions of the branched inner sinus (fig. 6). The variation in form of the sinus gland has been described in detail by Hanström (1947 a). In most stalk-eyed crustaceans the sinus gland lies in the eyestalk, but in *Gebia*, *Hippa* and in certain other Anomura the gland lies in the head in close proximity to the brain. In the Isopoda and in other eyestalkless species the gland lies in the head beside the brain.

In the living animal the sinus gland is easily recognizable by reason of its bluish white opalescence (Plate II (b)). This was first remarked by Brown and Cunningham (1939). In fixed and stained preparations also the sinus gland is easily distinguishable from surrounding tissues because it contains stored substances which colour intensely with acid dyes (e.g. eosin, acid fuchsin and light green). It has been shown, however, that materials in the sinus gland have an affinity for both basic and acid dyes and that the proportion of acidophil to basophil material varies with the physiological state of the animal. Gabe (1954) has shown that some products colour with the azocarmine of the azan method while others take up the aniline blue component. It has been found that some substances colour with the fuchsin of Mallory's trichrome stain, but others with the orange G (Enami, 1951 b). There is some evidence that the basophil material in the sinus gland may represent a transformation product of the acidophil substance. Pyle (1943) has shown that an acidophil reaction of the sinus gland of the American crayfish *Cambarus* changes to a basophil one after moulting and that there is moreover a corresponding reduction of material. Comparable changes have been recorded for the isopod *Oniscus asellus* by Gabe (1952 b). He has noted that during the intermoult period (Stage C of Drach, 1939) the sinus gland is entirely filled with acidophil droplets; during the stage before moulting (Stage D) the acidophil inclusions become less abundant, and immediately after the moult (Stage A) there are few acidophil droplets in the sinus gland; instead, the general coloration is blue after azan staining. This stage lasts only a few hours, and during the next period, while the integument hardens (Stage B), the sinus gland becomes filled once more with acidophil droplets. Gabe has observed that these appear first near the periphery of the organ. The change from acidophil to basophil inclusions may be a sign that active release of the secretory product is taking place.

The early descriptions of the sinus gland included a number of minute canals, which were said to penetrate the sinus gland and pass from the gland into the large blood sinus. It is now generally accepted that these so-called canals are in fact nerve fibre terminations (Bliss and Welsh, 1952). These authors suggested that the sinus gland of the crab *Gecarcinus* was little more than a mass of swollen nerve fibre endings, each of which contained acidophil secretory material and basophil granules, and that these contained the secretory material which had been detected in the sinus gland by earlier workers.

The question of whether or not the sinus gland contains secretory elements which manufacture an autochthonous substance has been disputed for many years. When the sinus gland was first described investigators believed that it manufactured the substances that it could be shown to contain, and that its rich innervation represented an elaborate control mechanism for the release of its stored products. Fibres leading from the medulla terminalis were observed by Hanström and were confirmed by Welsh (1941), who remarked also fibres leading from the brain to the sinus gland in *Cambarus*. Many of the early investigators, however, commented on the apparent lack of clearly distinguishable secretory elements in the sinus gland (Panouse, 1947; Pyle, 1943). Enami (1951 b) believed that he could find evidence of nuclear secretion in the sinus gland, but he since withdrew this idea and agreed with Bliss and Welsh (1952) that he wrongly interpreted as nuclei the bulbous terminations of axons in the sinus gland.

Fig. 4. Details of the structure of the sensory pore X organ of *Lysmata seticaudata*. Above, longitudinal section of the whole organ; below, enlarged details: the sensory nerve cells of the sensory pore, a group of the epithelioid cells and a group of onion bodies (the nerve endings of the axons of the X organ connective). *A.*, axons of the sensory nerve cells; *B.S.*, blood sinus; *B.Sp.*, blood space; *C.S.*, connective tissue sheath; *E.*, epithelioid cells or syncytium; *N.E.*, nerve ending of the neurosecretory nerves (onion bodies); *Nu*, nucleus of epithelioid cells; *Nu'*, nucleus of connective tissue sheath; *O.D.*, osmophilic droplets; *S.*, sensory nerve cell; *S.E.*, sensory endings; *S.P.*, sensory pore; *X.O.C.*, X organ connective. (Redrawn from Carlisle, 1953e.)

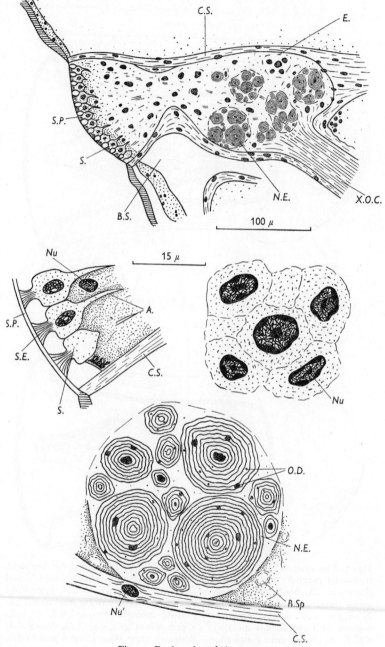

Fig. 4. *For legend see facing page.*

19

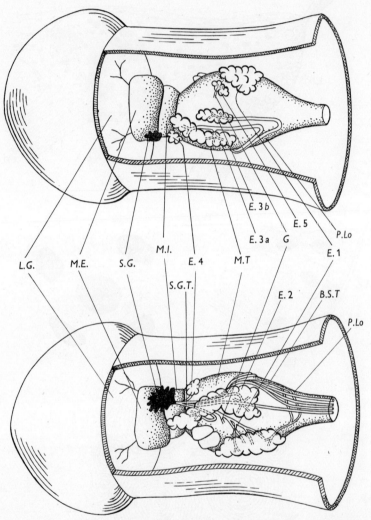

Fig. 5. The eyestalk of the macruran reptantian, *Cambarus virilis*, the American freshwater crayfish: upper, ventral dissection of the right eyestalk; lower, dorsal dissection. Double lines indicate neurosecretory fibre tract. *B.S.T.*, brain-sinus gland tract; *E.* 1–*E.* 5, groups of neurosecretory cells forming the ganglionic X organs; *L.G.*, lamina ganglionaris; *M.E.*, medulla externa; *M.I.*, medulla interna; *M.T.*, medulla terminalis; *P.Lo*, peduncle of optic lobe; *S.G.*, sinus gland; *S.G.T.*, combined sinus gland tract. (Redrawn after Bliss, Durand and Welsh, 1954.)

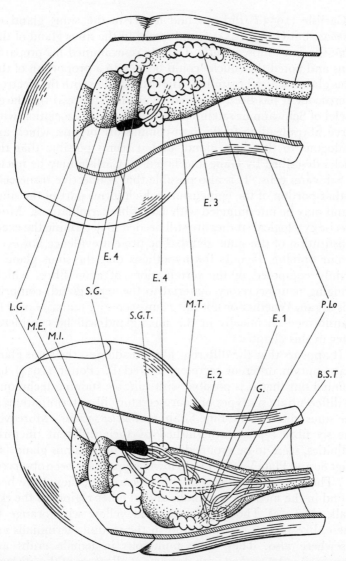

Fig. 6. The eyestalk of a crab, *Gecarcinus lateralis*: upper, dissection from the posterior surface of the right eyestalk; lower, dissection from the anterior surface of the right eyestalk. The lower drawing is correctly orientated; in the upper the eyestalk has been turned over so that it is lying upside down. Double lines indicate neurosecretory fibre tract. *B.S.T.*, brain-sinus gland tract; *E.* 1–*E.* 4, groups of neurosecretory cells forming the ganglionic X organs; *L.G.*, lamina ganglionaris; *M.E.*, medulla externa; *M.I.*, medulla interna; *M.T.*, medulla terminalis; *P.Lo*, peduncle of optic lobe; *S.G.*, sinus gland; *S.G.T.*, combined sinus gland tract. (Redrawn after Bliss, Durand and Welsh, 1954.)

Carlisle (1953 d) did not find nuclei in the sinus gland of *Lysmata*, but Gabe (1954) found nuclei in the sinus gland of the same species. Subsequently, Carlisle re-examined his preparations and noted that nuclei could be seen in a proportion of the sinus glands which he studied. In recent studies with the electron microscope it has been observed (Knowles, in press) that large nuclei of Schwann or satellite cells are found in association with nerve fibres leading to the post-commissure organs, which are analogous to the sinus gland, and it seems possible that the nuclei described by Gabe and noted by Carlisle may be nuclei of Schwann cells. It is also possible that connective tissue cells of that portion of the epineurium which forms part of the sinus gland may be intermingled with axon fibre terminations. More precise cytological studies are still needed to determine the exact constitution of the sinus gland. The present evidence however, in our opinion, favours the hypothesis that the sinus gland is mainly composed of the terminations of axon fibres which, bringing neurosecretory material to the sinus gland, comprise this organ. Whether or not this neurosecretory material may be transformed chemically in the sinus gland will be considered later in this chapter.

It appears that the different fibres leading to the sinus gland may contain different secretory materials. Potter (1954) has pointed out that it is possible with suitable staining techniques to differentiate six types of neurosecretory fibre terminations in the sinus gland of the Blue Crab, *Callinectes sapidus*. Moreover, the six fibre types, distinguished by their different tinctorial affinities, seem to be grouped separately in the sinus gland (see page 80 and Plate V (a)). The following types have been observed: (1) Those which stained red with azocarmine; these have been found in the medulla terminalis and in other regions of the eyestalk also. (2) Those which stained yellow with orange G; these, like type (1), were found in the medulla terminalis and elsewhere also. They were numerous in female crabs and appeared to be packed with droplets at all stages of the life cycle except the few days preceding the terminal moult which occurs just before sexual maturity. (3) Fibres which stained purple with azocarmine and aniline blue, found in the medulla terminalis. This type of fibre was rarely seen in males. (4) Fibres which stained red with aldehyde fuchsin; found in the medulla terminalis. (5) Fibres which stained orange with orange G;

22

these were restricted to the point of entry of the sinus gland nerve. (6) Fibres which stained blue with aniline blue; these, like type (5), were restricted to the point of entry of the sinus gland nerve.

The above fibre types contained inclusions each from 0·1 to 0·3μ in diameter. It is not yet clear how the release of these stored products is controlled. Possibly each fibre acts like a normal neurone and triggers the release of its contained substances or possibly there are additional fibres which are not neurosecretory which control the release of products from the neurosecretory fibre terminations. Potter observed five nerve fibres leading to the sinus gland of crabs which did not appear to be neurosecretory, but it is possible that they too were neurosecretory but that their contained products did not stain with the dyes that he used. The possible control of secretion in the sinus gland will be discussed later; for the present it will suffice to say that the sinus gland of all crustaceans examined carefully appears to consist mainly of the club-shaped terminations of fibres arriving from the optic centres and from elsewhere, and that in some species at least it seems likely that each fibre contains its own characteristic secretory product.

THE POST-COMMISSURE ORGANS

The first clear indication that central nervous tissues outside the eyestalk might contain chromactivating substances in crustaceans was given by Brown (1933) who found that the injection of an extract of the central nervous system of *Palaemonetes* was followed by the concentration of dispersed red pigments in the chromatophores of eyestalkless animals. Later experiments on other members of the Palaemonidae showed that the nerve cord, especially that part in the thorax, contains appreciable quantities of a white, pigment-concentrating hormone, and that the presence of this hormone could not be attributed to sinus gland activity (Knowles, 1939). Ablation experiments (Knowles, 1952) finally eliminated the possibility that the sinus glands are the only source of the white pigment concentrator. In a search for the source of this chromactivating substance in the central nervous system, attention was especially directed on the region of the circum-oesophageal connectives and nearby regions, because in 1940 Brown and Ederstrom had shown that this region was especially rich in chromactivating substances. The greatest amount of activity lay in the post-oesophageal commissure, especially near two slight swellings of the commissure in which a bluish green particulate substance could be seen and some cell bodies detected (Brown, 1946).

The post-oesophageal commissure is a very constant feature in most groups of the higher crustacea. Hanström and others have shown that it should be considered as part of the tritocerebrum and that it, the connectives and their ganglia represent part of the nervous system of the first post-oesophageal somite which has secondarily come into relation with the brain. Two fine nerves which leave the hinder margin of the commissure had for many years following the work of Police (1908) been considered as innervators of oesophageal muscles. The reason why chromactivating substances should be associated with this region did not seem clear, and so a detailed study of this region was undertaken by one of us (Knowles, 1951, 1953 a) in *Penaeus braziliensis* with the purpose of correlating physiological activity with histological structure. Different regions were extracted separately and the effects of these extracts on the chromatophore system were studied.

In preliminary experiments it was found that the greatest activity did not lie in the connectives, or in the commissure, but in the two fine nerves leaving the hinder margin of the commissure. Each of these nerves passed close to an oesophageal muscle, but did not apparently innervate it; instead it passed behind the muscle, turned forward once more around the muscle, and finally innervated a muscle which was attached at its base to the cephalic apodeme of the endophragmal skeleton and dorsally by a long tendon to the dorsal hypodermis (figs. 7, 8 and 9). Immediately before reaching this latter muscle the nerve appeared to broaden and form an extension, which took the form of a disc, 5 to 7μ in thickness and 150μ in diameter. It was found that in this lamella, formed by an extension of the epineurium, a delicately ramifying system of fine fibres could be observed, together with a number of fuchsinophil droplets. Extraction and injection experiments showed that this lamella was an extremely potent source of chromactivating substances. Fuchsinophil droplets were also found along the course of the post-commissure nerves, and it was shown that those regions which were richest in droplets yielded the most active extracts.

24

Subsequently it has been shown that the fine fibre ramifications in the lamellae derive from fibres which appear to originate in the brain, and the present evidence suggests that chromactivating substances are produced in some centre in the brain (probably the tritocerebral region), are transported along fibres to the post-commissure region and there are finally liberated into the blood stream through the lamellae or post-commissure organs, which in *Penaeus* lie adjacent to, and partially fused with, a blood sinus.

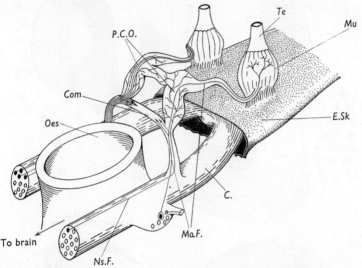

Fig. 7. A semi-diagrammatic view of the post-commissure organs of *Leander serratus* to show their relation to nearby structures. Each connective contains four neurosecretory fibres which run to the post-commissure organs (for a detailed view of the course of one of these see fig. 10); two motor fibres have also been seen traversing each post-commissure organ. In this figure, for the sake of clarity, only one neurosecretory fibre and one motor fibre are shown in the left connective and left post-commissure organ. *Ns.F.*, neurosecretory fibre; *Mo.F.*, motor fibre; *C.*, circum-oesophageal connective; *Com*, commissure; *P.C.O.*, post-commissure organs; *Oes*, oesophagus; *Mu*, muscle; *Te*, tendon; *E.Sk*, endophragmal skeleton.

Thus far the post-commissure organs have been studied in detail in *Penaeus braziliensis*, in the stomatopod *Squilla mantis* and in the prawn *Leander serratus*. They have not yet been detected in crabs, despite a search. In *Squilla* the lamellae lie on the surface of the oesophageal muscle over which the post-commissure nerve passes. In *Leander* the lamella forms immediately after the post-commissure nerve leaves the commissure, and the two

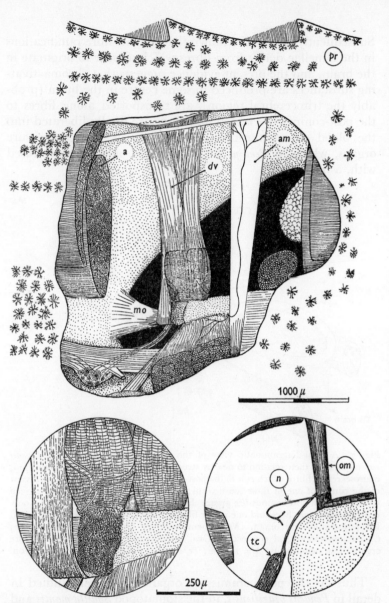

Fig. 8. The commissure region of *Penaeus braziliensis*, dissected from the left side. The smaller drawings represent the post-commissure region before and after the removal of the post-commissure organ and the dorsoventral muscles. This figure should be compared with fig. 9. *a*, muscle of antenna; *am*, adductor muscle of mandible; *dv*, tendon attached to dorsoventral muscle; *n*, post-commissure nerve; *om*, muscle to oesophagus; *pr*, posterior spine of the rostrum; *tc*, tritocerebral commissure; *mo*, oesophageal muscle. (Reprinted from Knowles, 1953a.)

26

lamellae formed by the two nerves are joined by a horizontal lamella which lies in a blood sinus. The form of these post-commissure organs is given at figure 10. Essentially the organs of the three species shown appear to be the same, and it is only their proximal or distal position which differs. In *Leander* each lamella appears to contain the branches of eight fibres, four passing down each connective from the brain, whereas in *Penaeus* ten fibres seem to supply the two lamellae. The number of fibres has not yet been ascertained in *Squilla*.

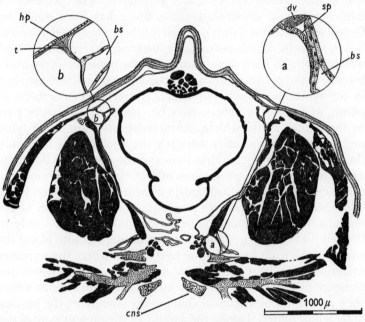

Fig. 9. A transverse section through *Penaeus braziliensis* at the level of the post-commissure organs, showing the relationship of these organs to adjacent blood sinuses. *a*, the post-commissure organ and associated structures; *b*, the point at which a dorsoventral muscle is attached to the hypodermis; *bs*, blood sinus; *cns*, central nervous system; *dv*, dorsoventral muscle; *hp*, hypodermis; *sp*, post-commissure organ; *t*, termination of the tendon from the dorsoventral muscle. (Reprinted from Knowles, 1953*a*.)

The tinctorial affinities of the fibres supplying the lamellae appear to differ from those of the motor fibres which pass through these lamellae and innervate muscles. When the region is removed from a freshly killed prawn and is placed in methylene blue the motor fibres stain first and later lose their colour, but

27

the fine ramifying fibres, though slower to take up the stain, retain it longer. Recently one of us (F.G.W.K.) has attempted to discover by electron microscopy whether the structure of these fine fibres differs from that of the motor fibres in any clearly detectable way.

When sections through the post-commissure nerves of *Squilla* were examined, using an electron microscope, it was possible to distinguish the neurosecretory fibres from the normal motor fibres by reason of the very great quantities of mitochondria which the neurosecretory fibres contained. The presence of mitochondria in crustacean nerve fibres has been noted by Geren and Schmitt (1954). These authors suggested that the Schwann cells which surround crustacean nerve fibres (and which have also been seen to surround the neurosecretory fibres leading to the post-commissure organs) may be actively engaged in the synthesis of materials which are secreted into the axo-plasm, and that the process may be energized at least in part by the mitochondria which, characteristically, are found lying peripherally, immediately beneath the axolemma. Certainly the presence of mitochondria indicates the possibility that they are implicated in the production of materials, and therefore the presence of so many mitochondria in neurosecretory axon fibres is of theoretical interest, as possibly indicating that an active manufacture of secretory material may take place not only in the cell body of the neurosecretory neurone, but also along the course of the axon fibre leading to the point where the secretory materials are released into the blood stream. Alternatively the presence of mitochondria might indicate that, in regions where they are found, biochemical changes are energizing the passage of secretory material along the axons. In the present state of our knowledge it is not possible to decide whether the mitochondria in neurosecretory fibres are more likely to be engaged in the manufacture of neurosecretory material or in its passage along the axon fibre; it is possible that they may be actively engaged both in the production of the material and in its transport.

The post-commissure organs, like the sinus glands, are essentially extensions of the epineurium, and appear to consist mainly of connective tissue containing innumerable fine branching fibres. Recent studies with the electron microscope have indicated that in the post-commissure organs of *Squilla* some of these fibres approach the surface but turn immediately below the

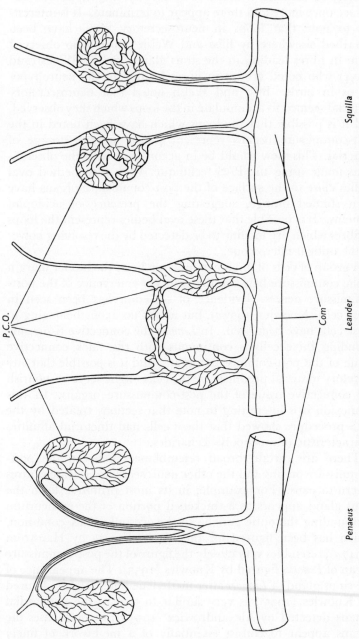

Fig. 10. Variation in the position of the post-commissure organs of three crustaceans. *P.C.O*, post-commissure organs; *Com*, commissure.

Penaeus   *Leander*   *Squilla*

P.C.O.

Com

29

surface, so forming a loop; subsequently they approach the surface once more and there appear to terminate. It is interesting to note that loops in neurosecretory fibres have been described elsewhere by Bliss and Welsh (1952) who observed them in fibres leading to the sinus gland, and by Wingstrand (1954) who noted groups in fibres leading to the neurohypophysis in birds. Bliss and Welsh noted that neurosecretory material seemed to accumulate in the loops which they observed, and it is possible that the loops which have been noted in the post-commissure organs represent places for the storage of material. This view would be in accordance with the observations made using the PAS technique. With this method oval bodies close to the surface of the post-commissure organs have been stained orange, suggesting the presence of acidophil proteins. It is possible that these oval bodies represent the loops of fibres which are too fine to be detected by the resolving power of the optical microscope.

A group of cells of unknown function lie at the hinder margin of the commissure between the points of emergence of the post-commissure nerves. Evidence of secretion has been seen in these cells (Knowles, 1953 a), but as yet no axons belonging to these cells have been seen. In *Leander* the connective tissue surrounding these cells is continuous with the thick connective tissue of the post-commissure organs, and it is possible that any secretory material produced by the cells might serve to nourish the connective tissue of the post-commissure organs. In this connexion it is interesting to note that sections treated by the PAS procedure showed that these cells had tinctorial affinities characteristic of mucopolysaccharides.

There are certain broad resemblances between the post-commissure organs and the other neurosecretory release centres in crustaceans. For example, in its most primitive form the sinus gland appears as a thickened portion of the epineurium surrounding the optic ganglia in the eyestalk. This condition, which has been figured for the Mysid *Eucopia* by Hanström (1947 a), resembles very closely the figure of the post-commissure organ of *Penaeus* figured by Knowles (1955). The appearance of the sinus gland of *Leander* after methylene blue staining, figured by Knowles (1955), is very similar to that of the pericardial organs detected by Alexandrowicz (1953 a); in both cases the organs appear to consist essentially of a meshwork of finely branched fibres many of which have a beaded appearance after methylene blue staining (Plate V (b)). It is possible that this beading may be due to aggregations of mitochondria at certain points along the course of the fibres, or it may represent the limits of separate Schwann cells; alternatively it may indicate droplets of secretion. Further studies are needed to determine the precise nature of the beading, which perhaps indicates heterogeneity along the course of the fibres.

It is interesting to speculate whether the post-commissure organs represent a primitive or advanced form of neurosecretory organ in the phylogeny of the Phylum Crustacea. The commissure itself is found in the most primitive living crustaceans, and in the Cladocera swellings on the commissure have been described which suggest the possibility of cell bodies in the commissure in the earliest forms. We have indicated elsewhere (p. 56) that the pigment-concentrating substance found in the head of the isopods examined seemed to reside in the commissure rather than in the eyestalk region, and it has been shown that the same general statement is true for the Stomatopod *Squilla*. These facts, taken together with the extremely primitive nature of the sinus gland in Mysids, indicates the possibility that in phylogeny the post-commissure organs may have preceded the sinus glands, but that during the evolution of the Decapoda the sinus glands assumed a greater importance. Thus the most elaborate sinus glands discovered so far are those in crabs, and it is interesting to note that in these forms the post-commissure organs have not so far been detected.

NEUROSECRETORY CELL GROUPS

Having examined two of the release centres where hormones are secreted from neurosecretory fibre terminations into the blood stream let us now examine the evidence for the identification of the cell bodies of these neurosecretory fibres.

Within recent years a number of investigators have published figures and descriptions of neurosecretory cells in many parts of the central nervous systems of crustaceans (Enami, 1931 a, b; Bliss and Welsh, 1952; Bliss, Durand and Welsh, 1954; Carlisle, 1953; Durand, 1956; Parameswaran, 1955; Matsumoto, 1956; and others). A survey of different neurosecretory cell types has recently been published by Durand (1956). He has described four cytologically distinct types of neurosecretory cells in the eye-stalk and brain of a crayfish, and has compared these types to neurosecretory cells described in other species by other workers.

There are, clearly, two criteria by which a neurosecretory cell can be recognized, namely, its appearance and the active substances which it may be shown to contain. According to E. Scharrer (1954), to whom we are primarily indebted for the concept of neurosecretion, 'Neurosecretory cells are neurons with Nissl bodies, dendrites, axons and neurofibrils. They produce granules and droplets of substances which can be stained by a variety of methods.... The neurosecretory cell can be recognised, therefore, by its cytological characteristics.' According to the morphological criterion, therefore, nerve cells which contain appreciable quantities of stainable substances may be suspected of neurosecretion, and it is on this basis that many cell groups in the central nervous systems of crustaceans have been described as 'neurosecretory cells'. In some cases the identification is supported by physiological evidence also. To a physiologist a most striking feature of neurosecretion is the fact that most neurosecretory cells, although present in the central nervous system and possibly similar in general structure and distribution to ordinary motor neurons, nevertheless *do not innervate any muscle or exocrine organ*. Their axons terminate in close proximity to a blood vessel or sinus and these axons can be shown by extraction and injection experiments to contain appreciable quantities of chemical substances which can also be found in the blood stream, and which have high biological activity on certain tissues (Carlisle and Knowles, 1953).

Ideally the identification of any cell as a neurosecretory cell should take account of both morphological characteristics and physiological activity, and in the case of certain cells associated with the sinus gland and the post-commissure organs these requisites have been fulfilled. A number of cell bodies in the brain, the optic ganglia and the thoracic sub-oesophageal ganglia have been shown by appropriate staining techniques to contain appreciable quantities of secretory material, and axon fibres leading from these cells have been shown to terminate in the sinus glands and post-commissure organs; physiologically active substances have been extracted from the regions of these fibre tracts and from the two release organs.

The sinus glands appear to be supplied by fibres originating in the eyestalks, the brain and the thoracic ganglia; the post-commissure organs seem to be supplied by fibres which originate in the tritocerebral region of the brain.

The neurosecretory system of the eyestalk is complex and it seems likely that in some species there may be more than one neurosecretory release centre. In brachyuran and reptantian decapods the sinus gland appears to be the main if not the only release centre, and fibres from many parts converge there (figs. 5 and 6). In natantian decapods, however, some apparently neurosecretory fibres appear to supply what has been termed the 'X organ' (fig. 3).

The X organ. During his search for secretory tissues in the eyestalks of crustaceans Hanström recorded a group of cells to which the name X organ was given. A survey of the earlier work on the X organ is given by Hanström (1939) in which he puts forward the hypothesis that the X organ represents the transformed sensory cells of a rudimentary eye papilla or sensory pore, and in which he points out that when the eye papilla or sensory pore is present it is always connected with the X organ in position and innervation. The choice of the name X organ dates from 1882, when Bellonci figured but did not describe in detail an organ in the head of the isopod *Sphaeroma*, to which he gave the letter X to denote unknown function. In 1905 Dohrn described a similar organ in the eyestalk of the mysid *Eucopia*, and showed that it lay close to a sensory papilla in the eyestalk. It is generally accepted that the typical X organ described by Hanström is found associated with a sensory pore or papilla wherever these are present, and it has been suggested (Knowles and Carlisle, 1956) that Hanström's X organ be termed the Sensory Pore X organ or Sensory Papilla X organ (SPX). We consider that it is desirable to designate this X organ by a very precise and specific name to avoid confusion with other cell groups which have been indiscriminately called X organs by various workers during the past decade.

Characteristically Hanström's X organ contains small acidophil droplets and 'larger irregularly shaped concretions of a concentric nature'. Hanström interpreted these concretions as accumulated products of secretion, but Carlisle (1953 d) has produced evidence to indicate that they are in fact the terminations of axon fibres coming from the medulla terminalis, and that each axon divides into many branches each of which terminates in a many-layered club-shaped body (Carlisle, 1953 d, e). Droplets of osmophilic and phloxinophilic secretion were seen lying between the layers. There is a general resemblance to the ensheathing scales of an onion seen in section (fig. 4). In the post-commissure organs also structures resembling the 'onion bodies' of the X organ can be seen in normal histological preparations. Under the electron microscope it appears that these scales are not exactly concentric but may be the coiled mesaxonal component of a Schwann or satellite cell ensheathing the axon fibre. It has been found that after very precise osmic fixation the coils are fairly tightly packed together, but that if there are osmotic changes during or after fixation the coils separate, and the appearance of an onion body is observed.

In addition to the onion bodies other cellular elements have been found in the X organs of different species. These include most commonly the sensory cells of the pore or papilla, and also isodiametric epithelium-type cells which show clear evidence of secretory activity (fig. 4); in some species at least some neurone cell bodies containing secretory material have also been observed (Hanström, 1939; Carlisle, 1953 d, e; Pyle, 1943).

The relation of the sensory papilla X organ to other structures in the eye-stalk is of great interest and importance. Carlisle (1953 b) has indicated that in *Lysmata* the onion body components of the X organ are the terminations of axon fibres, some of which originate in cell bodies which lie in the medulla terminalis, and others which appear to originate in the brain (see fig. 2). It has been suggested (Carlisle 1953 b; Knowles and Carlisle, 1956) that substances are produced in the cell bodies of the axons and transported along the axons to the onion bodies where they are stored preparatory to release. In *Lysmata* axons of the sensory cells of the X organ unite to form a nerve, the sensory nerve, which runs to the medulla terminalis. There is no evidence that these cells are secretory. The remainder of the X organ is occupied by cells of an apparently epithelial nature, whose cytoplasm contains numerous basophilic granules. Under certain conditions and at some seasons of the year large vacuoles may appear in the cytoplasm of some of these cells, containing amorphous heavily staining colloid.

The X organ of the Natantia is evidently a heterogeneous organ, comprising secretory cells of an epithelial nature, neurosecretory fibre terminations, neurosecretory neuron cell bodies and sense cells in the more primitive forms, but probably neurosecretory fibre terminations only in the more advanced forms. The fibres leading to it are entirely distinct from those leading to the sinus gland, as may be seen in figs. 2 and 3.

The Medulla Terminalis 'X organ'. In 1941 Welsh described in the eyestalk of *Cambarus* an organ which stained heavily with methylene blue and which he suggested might represent the X organ that Hanström had not been able to find in *Cambarus*. This organ, which lay in the medulla terminalis, has subsequently been described by Bliss and Welsh (1952), Passano (1951 *a, b*, 1952), Potter (1954), Bliss, Durand and Welsh (1954) as the X organ, but neither in position nor in structure does it resemble the X organ of Hanström and his pupils.

It is clear that the X organ originally described by Hanström is not precisely the same as the 'X organ' originally described by Welsh. In 1953 Carlisle and Passano realized that the X organ of the American workers and that of the European workers was not of the same structure and noted that the organs differed in different species. In the Decapoda Natantia the Hanström X organ and the cluster of secretory cells in the medulla terminalis are widely separated. In the Stomatopoda they lie close together in the medulla terminalis (Carlisle and Passano, 1953). In the Brachyura they form a single complex within the medulla terminalis; in the members of the Anomura so far studied the degree of separation of the two X organs lies intermediate between the two extremes found in crabs and shrimps. It cannot be too strongly emphasized that, in assessing the results of work published during the past decade, care should be taken to determine the intention of the author when the name X organ is used. We have pointed out (Knowles and Carlisle, 1956) that in some cases the name X organ has been used to denote the Hanström X organ, in others to denote the Welsh X organ; in yet others the intention is not entirely clear.

Recent studies of the eyestalks of crustaceans have shown that there are many groups of cells which show secretory activity, and that the interrelationships of these cells are generally complex (Bliss and Welsh, 1952; Knowles, 1955; Bliss, Durand and Welsh, 1954). The sinus gland seems to receive fibres from a number of different sources, but one source seems to be especially important, namely the medulla terminalis. All authors seem to agree that the large cluster of neurosecretory

3-2

cells in the medulla terminalis, the axons of which terminate in the sinus gland, represent a most important source, if not the most important source, of the hormones released by the sinus gland.

The first complete description of secretory cells in the medulla terminalis was given by Enami (1950-1). These cells, which he described as Beta cells, were large (about 50μ in diameter in the crab *Sesarma*), and were distinguished also by the secretory products which they contained. Many fine droplets were seen in the cytoplasm; some of these stained feebly with aniline blue, but others stained deeply. Enami noted that these granules could also be detected along the path of the axons arising from the cells with secretory activity, and in one case the granules were seen along the course of the sinus gland nerve for approximately two-thirds of its whole length. Evidence is given elsewhere (p. 8) that these cells in the medulla terminalis appear to be associated with the moulting cycle in crabs, and it is interesting to note that Durand (1956) has produced evidence that there is an accumulation of stainable material in these cells just before moult. Durand suggests that the release of a moult-inhibiting hormone is checked just prior to moult, and that as a consequence there is a concentration of this substance in those cells in which it is normally manufactured. This is so far the most satisfactory identification of a cell group with a physiological activity in crustaceans. It is to be hoped that during the next decade this method may be extended to other cell groups also.

The Beta cells described by Enami were also found by him in the brain and in the commissural ganglia. Enami, moreover, distinguished also two other cell types named α and γ cells, both of which were found in the brain and the eyestalks, and one of which (α cell) was found in the thoracic ganglion. Subsequently Parameswaran (1955) described three types of neurosecretory cells in the thoracic ganglion of the crab *Paratelphusa*. He considered that the most conspicuous type (which he named the A cell) corresponded to the A cells described previously by Matsumoto (1954) in the crab *Eriocheir*. Nayar and Parameswaran (1955) have suggested that the cyclical development of succinic dehydrogenase in the A cells suggests a probable significance of these cells in the regulation of metabolism of the crab *Paratelphusa*. Matsumoto (1954a) suggested that the B cells of the crab *Eriocheir* might contain chromactivating hormones.

It is evident that we may distinguish, by reason of their differences in shape and tinctorial affinities, a number of cell types in the central nervous system of crustaceans, and that the destination of their fibres and the evidences of secretion within these cells indicate that they may be neurosecretory.

CONTROL OF HORMONE RELEASE

Although we cannot yet with certainty identify particular functions with specific neurosecretory cells, it is clear that there are a number of histologically distinct cells which show signs of secretory activity, and that it is possible that each cell type may control a different activity. This suggestion leads on to the interesting problem—how is the control of the release of material from neurosecretory cells effected? It is possible that a neurosecretory cell can be stimulated by other nerve cells and can conduct nerve impulses along its axon to its ending, where resulting changes in membrane permeability may cause materials stored within the endings to be released into the blood stream. Alternatively it is possible that ordinary neurons terminate upon the endings of neurosecretory cells and effect changes in cell permeability at the neurosecretory cell fibre terminations. The evidence for these two possibilities has recently been reviewed by Bliss (1956). She considers that there is evidence that neurosecretory cells can, in addition to manufacturing hormones, propagate nerve impulses along their axons. According to this interpretation a neurosecretory cell itself effects release of the materials which it manufactures, and is stimulated to do so by impulses received synaptically from ordinary neurons of the central nervous system. If a single neurosecretory cell manufactured a particular hormone, then the stimulation of that cell would effect the release of its hormone from the axon fibre termination into the blood stream. According to this concept there is no need to postulate an independent secretory activity in the sinus gland, which can be considered as a collection of neurosecretory fibre terminations of various kinds, filled with various hormonal materials, the release of which is controlled by impulses travelling along the axons which contain the secretory materials. It has been suggested that an organ of this kind which consists primarily of the terminations of neurosecretory fibres, sometimes intermingled with other tissues (especially, of course, supporting connective tissue), and located

37

in or alongside the walls of blood vessels or blood cavities might be termed a neurohaemal organ (Carlisle and Knowles, 1953). Gabe (1954) has criticized this concept, especially in so far as it relates to the sinus gland. His reasons for so doing are based on his detection by histological means of substances which he considers to be produced in the sinus gland itself, and on the presence in the 'gland' of structures which he considers to be nuclei.

At present, as we have already remarked, there is little evidence which justifies a view that the secretory material present in the sinus gland and other neurohaemal organs is autochthonous and which at the same time excludes the possibility that the secretory material has been brought along axons from cell bodies located elsewhere.

Gabe (1952 b, 1953 c, 1954) considered that the histological evidence favours the concept of active secretion by the sinus gland. He has pointed out that simple trichrome stains allow one to distinguish a substance in the sinus gland which is different in staining properties from those materials found in an X organ and other neurosecretory tissues of the eyestalk. It is clear, however, that the identification of chemically distinguishable substances in an X organ and in the sinus gland (Turchini, 1953, quoted by Gabe, 1954) does not logically demand that an active secretion of hormonal material has taken place in the sinus gland, but, as Gabe (1954) has noted, may indicate a transformation of neurosecretory material; a transformation of material would provide substances with different staining properties.

There are a number of indications that the secretory materials in the adrenal medulla and in the neurohypophysis of mammals are stored as granules bounded by semipermeable membranes;

LEGEND TO PLATE III

(a) Section through small portion of sinus gland of *Squilla mantis* (× 44,000). Nerve-fibre terminations lying beneath a connective tissue sheath are shown, each containing many droplets of secretory material.

(b) A more highly magnified view of some of the 'droplets' shown in (a). There is some evidence that each 'droplet' may in fact represent secretory material lying within tubes of endoplasmic reticulum (× 132,000).

(c) A droplet in one of the neurosecretory fibres in a pericardial organ of *Squilla mantis*. A three-layered membrane ensheaths the secretory material (× 180,000).

(d) A section through a small portion of a pericardial organ of *Squilla mantis*. *cn*, connective tissue sheath; *cc*, cytoplasm of cell lying on surface of organ; *m*, mitochondrion; *s*, secretory droplets (× 22,000).

(e) Four droplets lying within a fine neurosecretory fibre in a post-commissure organ of *Leander serratus* (× 57,000).

PLATE III

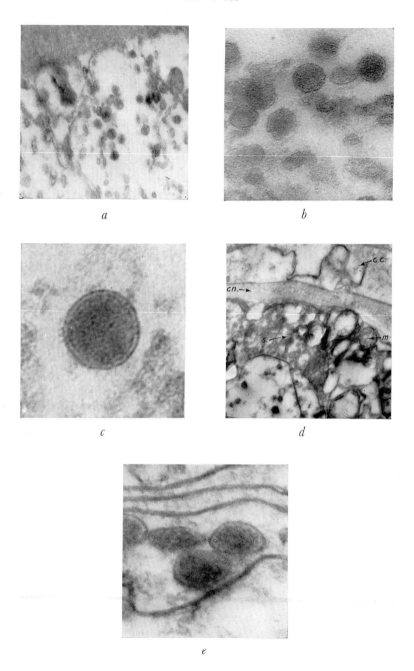

a

b

c

d

e

the evidence for this view is based partly on physiological experiments (Blaschko, Hagen and Welch, 1955) and partly on observations with the electron microscope (Palay, 1955). Comparable studies on crustaceans indicate that in these animals also endocrine substances are stored as discrete units bounded by membranes. One of us (F.G.W.K.) has recently studied with an electron microscope the fine structure of the neurosecretory fibre terminations in sinus glands, post-commissure organs and pericardial organs in *Squilla* and *Leander*. Some of the micrographs so far obtained are shown at Plate III. A three-layered membrane surrounding the secretory material can be distinguished, which in its dimensions (75–90 Ångström units) and appearance resembles the unit membranes described by Robertson (1958) and others in nervous tissues. It has been suggested that these membranes may be of a lipid or lipoprotein nature and that changes in permeability brought about by the arrival of a nerve impulse might permit the release of neurosecretory substances. This hypothesis accords with our present views on neurosecretion, namely that neurosecretory fibres might trigger the release of the substances that they contain; it also does not exclude the possibility that chemical transformations of the material might take place after it had been released from its bounding membrane.

To sum up, it is evident that the sinus gland and the post-commissure organs consist mainly of the terminations of neurosecretory fibres, and that in the case of the sinus gland there is evidence that different fibres contain chemically different secretory products. We cannot exclude the possibility that cellular elements present in the sinus gland bring about biochemical changes in the sinus gland, but as yet no convincing evidence of active secretion by discrete cells in the sinus gland has been proven. In the present state of our knowledge it would appear that the materials released by the sinus gland are brought to it along axon fibres from various cell bodies located in the optic ganglia, the brain and elsewhere, and that it and the post-commissure organs are centres for the release of products manufactured by cells in the central nervous system. It is possible that a 'blood-brain barrier' (as has been described for the vertebrates) prevents the release of materials from the nervous system to the blood except at the sinus gland, the post-commissure organs and at other neurohaemal organs.

39

CHAPTER 3

Colour Change

THE colour changes of crustaceans have been the object of considerable interest since they were first recorded by Krøyer (1842) in the prawn *Hippolyte*. Crustaceans are ubiquitous, and there are few waters that do not harbour one or more of their species; it is therefore not surprising to find that the range of colour and the diversity of colour changes in crustaceans is very wide. Some of the colour changes, slow, regular and predictable, are synchronized with the movements of the sun, the moon, and the earth, with dawn and nightfall, the tides and the seasons; others are adaptive responses to changes of illumination and background.

CHROMATOPHORES

Colour changes in crustaceans are accomplished by means of effector organs, the chromatophores, which are found directly underneath or within the hypodermis and also in the deeper-lying tissues of the body. Two kinds of colour change result from pigment movements in these chromatophores: (*a*) a morphological or quantitative colour change which involves a synthesis or destruction of the pigments within the chromatophores takes place when animals are subjected to particular conditions of illumination or background for some days or even weeks. It has been shown that these changes involve chemical alteration in the pigments and are not merely a translocation of pigments within the body (Brown, 1934); (*b*) a physiological or transitory colour change is brought about by movements of pigment granules within the chromatophores. This was first studied by Pouchet (1872–6), and was placed on a firm experimental basis by Keeble and Gamble (1900–5).

Crustacean chromatophores are elaborately branched cells containing one (monochromatic), two (dichromatic) or more (polychromatic) pigments; many chromatophores are multinucleate and appear to be groups of anastomosing cells. At one time it was thought that chromatophores were amoeboid cells, which sent out pseudopodia among the surrounding cells, but it is now generally accepted that the branched processes are permanently fixed in position and that the pigment granules stream along these predetermined pathways (see Plate I (c)). The independence of movement of the different pigments within a polychromatic chromatophore suggests that each pigment may possibly be contained in a physiologically distinct cell, although morphologically the cells appear to form a syncytium. Red and yellow carotenoid pigments are common. Lenel (1953a, b) has shown that in the shore crab, Carcinus maenas, β-carotene, xanthophyll and astaxanthine are present, the first two derived from the food and in part changed in the body to astaxanthine. It is evident that the red pigment in the chromatophores is closely linked biochemically with a blue pigment, for in dim light a blue pigment may be seen diffusing outwards in some species (Keeble and Gamble, 1904). This occurs, too, when red chromatophores contract violently as a result of an injection into the body of certain hormone extracts. Verne (1923) found the blue pigment of the lobster to be a carotenoid conjugated with a protein; the carotenoid, now known to be astaxanthine, thus becomes water soluble. The denaturation of the blue pigment by boiling, and its reversible denaturation at 60° C and pH 7, has been studied by Wald, Nathanson, Jencks and Tarr (1948).

A black pigment has been described in many crustacean chromatophores, and has frequently been termed melanin, but without sufficient biochemical evidence to justify this. It has been shown by Busnel and Drilhon (1948) that the dark pigment of Crangon (for long assumed to be melanin) is not melanin, for its solubilities are different, but it is similar to ommatin (Becker, 1941). The stalked eyes of crustaceans have a dark pigment which was formerly thought to be melanin, but it seems now that the eye pigment is ommatin (Linzen, personal communication).

A white light-reflecting pigment is almost universally found in the eyes and certain chromatophores of decapod crustaceans. It was formerly interpreted as guanin (Welsh, 1932), but there has as yet been no chemical confirmation of this, and Gwilliam (1950) has pointed to the differing solubilities of this white pigment in different species and has thrown a doubt on its guanin nature. Busnel and Drilhon (1948) have given evidence that the white pigment may be a pterin.

The distribution of pigments within chromatophores and the resultant colour patterns so formed varies greatly in the different crustacean groups. Broadly considered, polychromatic chromatophores are characteristic of the Decapoda Natantia, while monochromatic or bichromatic chromatophores are characteristic of the Isopoda, Stomatopoda, Astacura, Anomura and Brachyura.

COLOUR PATTERNS

(a) NATANTIA. The most elaborate colour changes among crustaceans are found in the Decapoda Natantia and are made possible by the polychromatic chromatophores arranged in groups to form patterns. There are two basic arrangements—broad masses, or bands of colour. In the Penaeidae and in *Crangon* the various chromatophores are dispersed fairly evenly though there is a tendency for the aggregation of chromatophores of like type. The result is that variations in the states of dispersal of a pigment in the different chromatophores leads to a somewhat blotchy pattern. In *Leander* and many other of the Palaemonidae, on the other hand, large dichromatic red-yellow chromatophores are arranged in bands, and the movement of pigment within these chromatophores either accentuates or diminishes this pattern (see Plate I (a)).

Brown and Wulff (1941 a, b) have given us a very complete account of the chromatophore types of *Crangon*. The pigment types of *Penaeus* are substantially similar (Knowles, 1953). Those of *Crangon* are: (a) monochromatic black, (b) dichromatic black-red, (c) trichromatic brown-yellow-red and (d) tetrachromatic black-white-yellow-red chromatophores. In *Penaeus* there are dichromatic red-yellow, trichromatic red-yellow-blue and tetrachromatic red-yellow-blue-white chromatophores. The difference between *Penaeus* and *Crangon* may be explicable by the fact that *Crangon* seems to differ from other Natantia in the possession of ommatin in chromatophores.

Detailed descriptions of other natantian pigment patterns have been given for *Palaemonetes* (Perkins, 1928; Perkins and Snook, 1931; Brown, 1934, 1935 a, b), for *Leander* (Carstam, 1942; Panouse, 1946; Knowles, 1952, 1955), and for *Hippolyte* by Keeble and Gamble (1904). These last authors considered

42

the development of the chromatophore system, and Carstam (1949) has discussed this in relation to the presence of chrom-activating hormones. The distribution of the various kinds of chromatophore, though in general fairly constant for any species, sometimes varies intraspecifically (Keeble and Gamble, 1904; Carlisle, 1955).

(*b*) BRACHYURA. The fiddler crab, *Uca pugilator*, which has been the subject of many physiological studies in colour change, has a chromatophore arrangement characteristic of most Brachyura. Three types of monochromatic chromatophores are present, containing black, red and white pigments respectively. The chromatophores of brackish water crabs of the genus *Sesarma* which has been studied by Enami (1950, 1951*a*, *b*) seem to differ slightly in detail from those of *Uca*. *Sesarma* has, like *Uca*, monochromatic black, red and white chromatophores, but in addition, vermilion ones. The different kinds of chroma-tophores appear to be scattered throughout the hypodermis, and they do not form striking colour patterns.

(*c*) ISOPODA. The authors who have worked on Isopods agree that colour change is effected by two types of monochromatic chromatophore: numerous reddish brown chromatophores (generally stated to contain melanin but more probably contain ommatin) and less frequent white chromatophores. A very com-plete survey of work on this subject has been given by Suneson (1947).

THE RESPONSES OF CHROMATOPHORES

There are three general kinds of responses of crustacean chroma-tophores to environmental factors.

(*a*) A RESPONSE TO TOTAL ILLUMINATION. Normally the greater the illumination the greater the degree of dispersal of the chromatophore pigments, both dark and light. When a small portion of the leg of *Uca* was shielded and the whole animal was illuminated, a normal dispersal of the black pigment took place in the illuminated portion, but not in the shielded area (Brown, Guyselman and Sandeen, 1949). A change of white pigments in response to change of illumination continues after the removal of eyes and eyestalks (Stephenson, 1934; Knowles, 1939), and it has been shown that some movement of the white pigments in response to change of illumination occurs even in isolated

43

chromatophores (Knowles, 1940). The interpretation of these effects of illumination on pigment movements is, however, a controversial and challenging problem. Brown, Sandeen and Webb (1948) found that the red pigment of eyeless *Palaemonetes* remained fully dispersed at all values of illumination and in darkness. Clearly the general statement that chromatophores are more expanded in light than in darkness is not applicable to all species, and it seems possible that we may have to seek for a more elaborate explanation of this phenomenon than at first seemed necessary. Chromatophore pigments are affected by blood-borne hormones, and the possibility that illumination is having an effect by sensitizing the chromatophores to the hormones activating them must be considered. Brown and Sandeen (1946) found by comparative injection experiments in *Uca* in light and darkness that illumination appeared to augment the action of the injected material on the chromatophores. Unfortunately it was difficult in these experiments to eliminate the possibility that light might be releasing blood-borne chromactivators in injected animals. In retinal pigment experiments, however, it was found that after sinus gland removal illumination had no apparent effect on the distal retinal pigment, but that in intact animals the retinal pigment in an exposed eye was more affected than in a covered eye of the same individual (Knowles, 1950). These results indicated that light might sensitize the distal retinal pigment to a hormone activating it.

(*b*) RESPONSE TO TEMPERATURE. If the temperature is raised above the normal range to which a crustacean is accustomed, white pigments are dispersed and dark pigments are concentrated. The result is that at these higher temperatures the body reflects more, and absorbs less, radiant energy. This response, therefore, seems to act as a body-temperature-regulating mechanism (Brown, 1949). Here again the precise part played by hormones has not yet been ascertained.

(*c*) AN ALBEDO RESPONSE. This is often called the background response and is regulated by the ratio of incident to reflected light striking the eye. In this response the dark light-absorbing pigments typically disperse and the paler light-reflecting pigments concentrate when the animal is upon an illuminated black background. The pigments assume the opposite condition upon a white background. Differential movements of red, yellow, black and white pigments permit an adaptation to the colour as well as the shade of the background. These albedo responses seem to be entirely under hormonal control.

(d) PERSISTENT RHYTHMS. Various authors have remarked that the pigments within the chromatophores and the eyes of crustaceans may alter in position in animals kept under constant conditions of illumination and temperature, and that these changes may be interpreted as persistent rhythms in phase with solar and lunar changes. Brown and his pupils have suggested that the rhythms of pigment movement and oxygen consumption in crustaceans may be controlled by two centres, one labile and readily modified by imposed environmental changes, the other more stable and conservative in its response to environmental change. The evidence for this view has been recently summarized by Stephens (1957).

It is clear that chromatophores are regulated by a complex of total illumination, temperature and the shade and colour of the background superimposed on fundamental rhythms of colour-change. The different states of a chromatophore have been described as 'expansion' or 'contraction', though it is generally accepted that the fine processes of a chromatophore are fixed in position in the hypodermis and that the colour changes are brought about by the movements of the pigment granules along fixed pathways, possibly by streaming movements of the cytoplasm. In those forms with more than one type of pigment the overall colour of the animal may sometimes seem dull, but under the microscope it will be seen that it is the result of an interplay of brilliant pigments of many colours moving independently of one another. We must now examine the mechanism whereby these pigment movements are regulated.

THE CONTROL OF PIGMENT MOVEMENTS WITHIN CHROMATOPHORES

The first experiments designed to discover a mechanism for chromatophore control in crustaceans were performed by Pouchet (1872–6) who found that if the eyes were removed from a prawn the animal became dark and lost its ability to change colour in response to different backgrounds. Pouchet then tried to demonstrate a nervous control of the chromatophores by cutting the ventral nerve cord, but these experiments were without effect. Matzdorff (1883), working on the isopod *Idotea*, was

45

also of the opinion that the chromatophores were under nervous control, but also was unable to demonstrate this experimentally. In spite of these negative results obtained by severing nerves, many investigators continued to suggest that crustacean chromatophores were controlled by nerves (Keeble and Gamble, 1900–5; Fröhlich, 1910; Menke, 1911; Degner, 1912a, b; Piéron, 1914; etc.). Finally, however, it was shown that the movement of pigment in crustacean chromatophores was under hormonal, not nervous, control. Perkins (1928), working on the prawn *Palaemonetes*, and Koller (1928), studying the shrimp *Crangon*, independently showed that the blood system contained substances which affected chromatophore pigments and that interruption of the blood supply had effects on the chromatophores, whereas interruption of nerves did not. Perkins showed that the eyestalks were a very potent source of a dark-pigment-concentrating substance. Numerous later investigators confirmed this and in addition indicated the possibility that dark-pigment-dispersing substances might also be present in crustaceans (Kropp and Perkins, 1933; Hosoi, 1934; Brown, 1935a, b; Carlson, 1936; Hanström, 1937; Abramowitz, 1937a, b; Kleinholz and Welsh, 1937; Sawaya, 1939; Ståhl, 1938a, b; etc.). Extracts prepared from the eyestalks appeared to have very potent pigment-concentrating effects and so as a result of these early physiological experiments a search was made for some organ of a secretory nature in the eyestalk which might be the source of the pigment-activating hormones; in due course this led to the discovery of the sinus gland.

The sinus gland was first detected by Hanström (1933) and has since then been described in some detail by Hanström (1937a, b) and by his students Sjögren (1934), Carlson (1936), Ståhl (1938a, b), and Carstam (1942) and more recently by Panouse (1946), Hanström (1947a, b), Enami (1951a, b), Gabe (1952a, b, c), Bliss and Welsh (1952), Carlisle (1953 d) and Bliss, Durand and Welsh (1954). A detailed account of this organ is given elsewhere in this book (pp. 13–23). In 1935 Hanström showed that the most potent pigment-activating extract was obtained from that portion of the eyestalk in which the sinus gland lay. Brown (1940, 1942) extended this observation by demonstrating that it was possible to recognize the sinus gland in the living animal on account of its bluish white opalescence when viewed by reflected light (see Plate II (b)), and that the sinus gland, though normally comprising about one-hundredth the volume of the soft tissue of the stalk, possessed about eighty per cent of the chromactivating activity. Furthermore, Brown, Ederstrom and Scudamore (1939) were able to remove the sinus glands from the eyestalks of living *Palaemonetes*, and noted that after this operation there was a complete dispersal of the red pigments in the chromatophores regardless of the colour of the background. Previous to this observation, investigators prepared a hormone extract from whole eyestalks, but subsequently, and especially recently, there has been a tendency to prepare extracts from sinus gland alone freed from surrounding tissues (Knowles, Carlisle and Dupont-Raabe, 1956).

After the discovery of the sinus gland many attempts were made to separate and identify the chromactivating substance present in eyestalk extracts. At once certain difficulties became apparent. First it became clear that more than one chrom-activating substance was present in eyestalk or sinus gland extracts. For instance, the dark pigments in the fiddler crab *Uca* were *dispersed* by extracts which *concentrated* the dark pigments of *Palaemonetes* (Carlson, 1936; Abramowitz, 1937a, b), and Brown and Scudamore (1940) showed by reciprocal injection experiments and by differential solubility analyses that in a number of different crustaceans a fraction of eyestalk extract soluble in 100 % ethyl alcohol had a predominantly '*Palaemonetes*-concentrating' effect, whereas the residue after alcohol extraction had mainly a '*Uca*-dispersing' effect.

In 1941 Brown and Wulff reported that even within a single species extracts with different effects on the chromatophore system could be prepared. They extracted eyestalk extracts of *Crangon* in alcohol and found that the alcohol-soluble fraction concentrated the black chromatophores of the body but were without effect on those of the telson and uropods; on the other hand, water extraction of the alcohol-insoluble residue resulted in an extract which concentrated the chromatophores of both the body and the tail. It was clear that more than one chrom-activating substance could be extracted from the eyestalks of crustaceans if suitable techniques were employed. The complexity of the problem of separating and identifying crustacean chromactivating hormones was further emphasized by the work of Brown and his students on the tritocerebral commissure region of *Crangon*. Brown and Klotz (1947) first extracted the

47

commissure region in pure methyl alcohol or isopropyl alcohol and then made an extract of the alcohol-insoluble residue in sea water. The alcohol-soluble fraction contained a body-lightening hormone, but the alcohol-insoluble fraction contained a body- and tail-darkening hormone. It seemed that the normal concentrations and dispersals of the black pigment in the chromatophores of *Crangon* might be due to the interaction of at least three, and possibly four, substances. It therefore seemed essential to devise some method of differential extraction of chromactivating substances before attempting chemical analysis. Experiments were therefore carried out on *Leander serratus*, using paper electrophoresis as the method for separating different chromactivators (Carlisle, Dupont-Raabe and Knowles, 1955; Knowles, 1955; Knowles, Carlisle and Dupont-Raabe, 1955). In these experiments we found evidence for the presence of a number of chromactivating substances in extracts of the sinus glands and post-commissure organs, some of the substances being active on different chromatophore types and some having antagonistic effects on the same pigment.

The colour pattern of *Leander serratus* seems to be typical of members of the Palaemonidae. It is brought about by (*a*) small dichromatic red-yellow chromatophores distributed evenly over the body and the tail; (*b*) large dichromatic red-yellow chromatophores regularly arranged to form bands of colour; (*c*) large trichromatic white-red-yellow chromatophores distributed in a scattered but regular fashion and which contribute to the pattern of the body (see Plate I (*b*)).

One chromactivating substance which affected only the dark pigments of types (*a*) and (*b*) seemed to be particularly abundant in extracts of the sinus gland and the post-commissure organs of *Leander* and in the corpora cardiaca of the stick insect *Carausius* and of the silk-worm *Bombyx*. We have named this the A-substance (Knowles, 1955; Knowles, Carlisle and Dupont-Raabe, 1955; Lerma, Dupont-Raabe and Knowles, 1955). It was electropositive at pH 7·5–7·8; it was relatively immobile under the conditions of electrophoresis used, denoting either that it is a large molecule or bears little charge, or both; it did not pass through cellophane membranes readily; after chromatography in N-propanol-aqueous ammonia it had an Rf value between 0·3 and 0·35; it was sometimes closely associated with a fluorescent substance, but appears to be active without it; it dis-

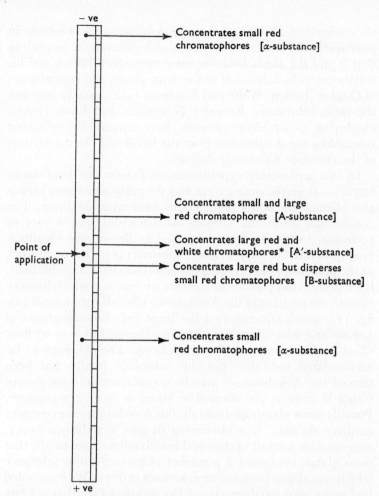

Fig. 11. The distribution of chromactivating substances on a paper strip after electrophoresis. The substances were contained in extracts of the post-commissure organs of *Leander serratus* and were separated by electrophoresis at 320 V., 5 hours, 0·8 mA/cm., in phosphate buffer of pH 7·8. (Modified from Knowles, 1956.)

* Found in extracts of the post-commissure organs of *Squilla*; detected in, but not separated from, *Leander* extracts.

appears from extracts which are allowed to stand for some hours at room temperature; and its activity can be destroyed by treatment with a trypsin extract (Knowles, Carlisle and Dupont-Raabe, 1956).

The A-substance had a very strong effect on the large red and the small red chromatophores of *Leander serratus*, concentrating their pigments. We found that the A-substance was soluble in pure methanol and there are reasonable grounds for suspecting that it and the alcohol-soluble substance which Brown and his collaborators had detected in the sinus glands and commissures of *Crangon* (Brown, Webb and Sandeen, 1952), may be one and the same substance. Recently Fingerman and Lowe (1957), employing paper electrophoresis, have separated a substance resembling the A-substance from the brain and the connectives of the crawfish, *Cambarella shufeldti*.

In our preliminary experiments on *Leander* the A-substance extracted from the sinus glands and the post-commissure organs also affected the white pigments by concentrating them. The A-substance from the corpora cardiaca did not, a fact in accordance with the results obtained by Brown and Meglitsch (1940), Hanström (1937b) and Thomsen (1943). In recent work on the post-commissure organs of *Squilla* (Knowles, unpublished), it has been found possible to separate a substance, which lies very close to the position of the A-substance after electrophoresis (see fig. 11), which concentrated the large red chromatophores of *Leander* and also the white chromatophores, but was without effect on the small red chromatophores. The evidence so far accumulated indicates that this substance (which has been termed the A'-substance) may be transformed into the A-substance if extracts are allowed to stand at room temperature. Possibly sinus glands also contain this A'-substance, but corpora cardiaca do not. It is interesting to note that Brown (1944) suggested, as a result of chemical inactivation experiments, that sinus glands contained a precursor chromactivating substance which was absent from corpora cardiaca extracts. We have noted in *Leander*, and Sandeen (1950) has noted in *Uca*, that a white pigment activator disappears from commissure extracts when they are allowed to stand at room temperature.

Paper electrophoresis of extracts of the sinus glands, post-commissure organs and corpora cardiaca revealed two substances which effect concentration of the small red chromatophores of *Leander serratus*; one was electro positive at pH 7·5 and the other was electro negative. These substances, which we have called alpha-substances, were found only in extracts which were allowed to stand for a short time. It has been suggested (Knowles, Carlisle and Dupont-Raabe, 1955; Knowles, 1955) that these substances represent disintegration products of the A-substance.

Boiled extracts did not appear to contain the alpha substances, which supports the suggestion that they arise by enzymatic transformation of the A-substance.

Recently Östlund and Fänge (1956) have described methods for the purification of a chromactivating substance from the eyestalks of *Pandalus borealis*, which concentrated the red chromatophores of *Leander*. They suggested that it may be identical with one of the alpha substances, though this identification is not yet certain. In their paper Östlund and Fänge suggested the possibility that the substance they had isolated might be an aromatic amine, but in a recent communication to the conference on neurosecretion at Lund (1957) they have stated that their substance appears to be strongly acidic and may possibly be of the nature of an acidic polypeptide. It could be inactivated by treatment with trypsin or chymotrypsin, the latter being especially effective in this respect.

Thus far, therefore, four distinct pigment-concentrating substances have been separated from extracts of *Leander* eyestalks and post-commissure organs, namely (*a*) an A-substance which concentrates the red pigments in all *Leander* chromatophores; (*b*) an A'-substance which concentrates the white pigments and the red pigments in the large red chromatophores; (*c*) two substances (one positively charged, the other negatively charged at pH 7·48) which affect the red pigments in the small chromatophores only. There is also evidence for pigment-dispersing substances in the neurosecretory organs of natantian decapods.

The electrophoresis experiments have separated a substance from the post-commissure organs of *Leander* which we have called the B-substance. Unlike the A-substance it is electro negative at pH 7·8, but resembles the A-substance in its relative immobility under the conditions of experiment and in its inability to pass through cellophane membranes; it is relatively unstable and disappears from extracts which are allowed to stand at room temperature. Like the A-substance it concentrates the large red chromatophores of *Leander*, but unlike the A-substance it *disperses* the pigment in the red chromatophores of the body and the tail. There appear to be many similarities between this B-substance of *Leander* and the alcohol-insoluble fraction of the *Crangon* commissure extract isolated by Brown and Klotz (1947). Figerman and Lowe (1957) have also detected a B-substance in their experiments on *Cambarella* extracts.

It has been claimed by Brown and Wulff (1941) that a white pigment disperser is present in extracts of the sinus gland. We have some evidence (reported in Knowles, 1955) that the sinus gland of *Leander* is formed of three distinct parts (fig. 3), each comprising the terminations of certain distinct nerve fibres, and that it is possible to separate these portions and to make extracts of them separately. The portion which receives fibres from the medulla terminalis X organ seemed to contain a substance that concentrated white chromatophore pigments (A'-substance?), but the remainder of the sinus gland seemed to contain a white pigment disperser; it seems possible that a white-pigment-dispersing substance might mask the effects of a white-pigment-concentrating substance if both these substances were present together in extracts of whole sinus gland (Carlisle, unpublished).

BRACHYURA. There have been various indications that the predominant chromactivators controlling pigment movements in the Brachyura differ from those found in the Decapoda Natantia. Removal of the eyestalks has a different effect in *Uca* from that previously described for the Natantia. After eyestalk ablation *Uca* pales as during the normal nocturnal phase in this genus, and an injection of eyestalk extract is needed to restore the normal dark diurnal colour (Carlson, 1936). The necessary substance is found in the eyestalks of a great number of crustaceans (Brown and Scudamore, 1940), and is found in *Uca* in high concentrations in the optic ganglia and sub-oesophageal ganglia, and in lower concentrations in the thoracic nerve cord and connectives (Sandeen, 1950). Bowman (1949) has reported that extracts of the central nervous system of the crab *Hemigrapsus oregonensis* cause dispersal of black pigment in animals of the same species.

The melanophore-dispersing substance of *Uca* (frequently described as the *Uca*-darkening substance) is evidently not the same as the *Palaemonetes*-lightening substances (Brown and Scudamore, 1940). Eyestalk extracts of various species were tested on eyeless *Palaemonetes* and *Uca*, and it was found that at one extreme was *Crangon* with a great effect on *Uca* black and a relatively small effect on *Palaemonetes* red chromatophores, and at the other extreme was *Palaemonetes*, extracts of which had a strong effect on its own chromatophores but a weak effect on those of *Uca*. It was shown that after extraction of various eyestalks in pure ethyl alcohol the alcohol-soluble fraction had a strong effect on *Palaemonetes* red pigment but a weak one on *Uca* black pigment. Conversely the alcohol-insoluble fraction had a strong effect on *Uca* black pigment but a weak one on *Palaemonetes* red pigment. The alcohol-soluble fraction is evidently the A-substance of the Natantia and is clearly different from the *Uca* black pigment disperser. It is not yet clear why *Palaemonetes* should contain the *Uca*-dispersion substance. There is moreover suggestive evidence that the '*Uca* disperser' is not restricted to crustaceans. Brown and Cunningham (1941) have shown that extracts of the central nervous system of *Limulus* contain a substance which disperses *Uca* black pigments but is without effect on dispersed red pigments of *Palaemonetes*. Abramowitz (1936*a*, *b*, 1938) determined the action of crustacean eyestalk extract upon fish, amphibian and reptilian melanophores and the action of intermedin upon *Uca* melanophores. In the light of this information and the very closely similar solubilities of the two materials in a variety of solvents, he concluded that the substance in the crustacean eyestalk extract was very similar to intermedin, though a number of facts indicated that they were not identical. Intermedin had an action on *Uca* black pigment, though there was no significant influence of intermedin on the red pigment of *Palaemonetes*. Hanström (1937*b*) had similarly found no significant action of intermedin on the red pigment of *Leander*. Thus the evidence so far presented indicates that crab eyestalks contain a chromactivating hormone different from those substances present in the Natantian eyestalks, and that the melanophore-disperser in *Uca* resembles the melanophore disperser found in certain vertebrate tissues.

It is interesting to note that in addition to the '*Uca*-dispersing substance' the eyestalk extracts of *Uca* apparently contain the A-substance although its effects are sometimes masked by a red pigment disperser. Enami (1950, 1951*a*, *b*) studied the crab *Sesarma* and reported that the red pigments in the chromatophores of this animal were concentrated by extracts of the sinus gland and also by extracts of the thoracic ganglion, commissural ganglion and various ganglia of the eyestalk. These extracts also concentrated the red pigments in *Paratya compressa*, a shrimp whose normal chromatic behaviour has been described by Nagano (1942). In 1950 Brown showed that the alcohol-soluble fraction of *Uca* eyestalk extract concentrated previously dispersed red pigments in the monochromatic red chromatophores of *Uca*, but that the alcohol-insoluble fraction seemed to antagonize the red-concentrating fraction, which may explain why Abramowitz (1937*a*) found that injections of whole eyestalk extracts into eyeless animals caused red pigment dispersion.

The red-pigment-dispersing substance detected by Brown (1950) was first believed by him to be identical with the *Uca*-dispersing substance, but subsequently Brown and Fingerman (1951) found that the red-pigment-dispersing substance was relatively insoluble in pure isopropyl alcohol, whereas the *Uca*-dispersing substance went readily into solution.

The exact relationship between the *Uca*-red-dispersing factor, the B-substance of the Natantia and the *Crangon*-darkening substance (CDH) is still obscure. There appear to be many general resemblances of distribution, solubility, etc., and we are of the opinion that the dispersal of red pigment in crustacean chromatophores is controlled by a single substance. It has been claimed by Brown and Saigh (1946), however, that the *Crangon*-darkening substance could not be detected by them in the Brachyura. We have observed that the B-substance of *Leander* is unstable and disappears rapidly from extracts allowed to stand at room temperature. Possibly it may be present in Brachyura in relatively small amounts and will not be detectable if extracts are allowed to stand for even a short time. It is evident that further investigation is needed before the red-pigment-dispersing substance of crabs can be identified with other red-pigment-dispersing substances in crustaceans; the method of paper electrophoresis seems to be particularly suitable for a comparative study of this kind.

There is some evidence for the presence of a black pigment concentrator in crabs. Enami (1943*a*, *b*) found that injections of extracts of the sinus glands or of cerebral or abdominal ganglia induce paling in *Uca dubia*, and Brown and Scudamore (1940) and Webb, Bennett and Brown (1953) found that weak extracts of the eyestalk are about twice as effective in causing dispersal of black pigment in the day-time than after 8 p.m. This latter observation could be explained by the supposition that there is a black pigment concentrator present in the eyestalk during the night or that there is less black pigment disperser present during the night than during the day. Enami (1950, 1951*a*, *b*) has reported that the black pigments of *Sesarma* were concentrated by extracts of the brain and the medulla terminalis of this genus.

54

Fingerman (1956) has given evidence for a black pigment concentrator in *Uca*.

There has been some suggestion also that white pigment concentrators and dispersers may be present in crabs (Brown, 1948*b*; Enami, 1950, 1951*a*, *b*).

To sum up, it appears that the following chromactivators may be present in crabs; (1) a red pigment concentrator (Brown, 1950); (2) a red pigment disperser (Brown, 1950; Brown and Fingerman, 1951); (3) white concentrators and dispersers (Brown, 1948*b*; Enami, 1950, 1951*a*, *b*); (4) a black disperser (Carlson, 1936, and later workers), and probably also a black pigment concentrator (Webb, Bennett and Brown, 1953; Enami, 1950, 1951*a*, *b*; Fingerman, 1956).

ISOPODA. The authors who have worked on isopods agree that colour change is effected by two types of monochromatic chromatophore: numerous reddish brown chromatophores (generally stated to contain melanin) and less frequent white chromatophores. (The early work has been reviewed by Suneson, 1947.) There is evidence that a black-pigment-concentrating substance is present in the head region of isopods. Kleinholz (1937*b*) found that an extract prepared from the head of *Ligia baudiniana* injected into the same species was followed by a concentration of previously dispersed dark pigments, and this has been confirmed for *Idotea neglecta* and *Idotea emarginata* by Suneson (1946) and by Carstam and Suneson (1949), for *Sphaeroma* by Okay (1945) and for *Ligia exotica* by Enami (1941*b*) and Nagano (1949). There is considerably less evidence for the presence of a melanophore-dispersing hormone. Enami (1941*b*) has brought forward evidence that the head of *Ligia exotica* contains a substance which disperses melanin in this species; he observed, however, that an injection of a head extract was followed first by a concentration and then a dispersal of the melanin. It is possible that the isopod head contains both melanophore-expanding and melanophore-contracting hormones and that the effects of the latter predominate in most cases. The incretory organs of the isopod head and their relation to the chromatophore system have been studied by Amar (1948, 1950, 1951).

Many authors have attempted, on the basis of reciprocal injection experiments, to identify chromactivators in the isopods with chromactivators in the macruran decapods, but have found great difficulty in interpreting their results (Knowles and Carlisle, 1956). It seems clear that a hormone concentrating the dark pigments of isopods is produced in some part of the head. The results of the work by Suneson (1946) suggest that this might be the A'-substance; injections of *Idotea* head extracts into *Leander* gave the typical A' reaction, concentrating red pigment in dichromatic chromatophores and white pigment in the white chromatophores, though leaving some red pigment in monochromatic chromatophores unaffected. We have made some preliminary observations (unpublished) which support this view and suggest that the tritocerebral commissure may be the site of this substance. It is not yet known if there is any of the A-substance present in isopods, but if there is it seems unlikely that it has a concentrating effect on the dark pigment of isopods, for extracts of the eyestalks of *Leander adspersus* (Suneson, 1947) and those of the head of the orthopteran insect *Chorthippus* (Hanström, 1940), which might be expected to contain great quantities of the A-substance, dispersed pigments in isopods. Östlund and Fänge have recently reported that the chromactivator they have isolated from the eyestalk of *Pandalus* appeared to have no effect on isopods. Until purified solutions containing the A-substance alone are tested on isopods, this problem cannot be resolved. Meanwhile it seems most reasonable to suggest that the dark pigments of isopods are concentrated by a substance analogous (if not identical) to the A'-substance of decapods and that this may be produced in the tritocerebral commissure region.

THE NUMBER AND NATURE OF CHROMACTIVATING HORMONES

At first sight the results of injection and ablation experiments and of chemical analyses seem to present a very confused picture of crustacean chromatophore control, but there are certain broad resemblances between the different species studied which indicate the possibility of relatively few chromactivating substances widely distributed in the phylum Arthropoda. The distribution and activity of these may be summarized in a table.

This is clearly not intended as a comprehensive list of chromactivating substances which have been isolated from arthropod tissues, nor, in view of the scanty information which we have on the chemistry of the substances, can we be sure that the substances with apparently similar effects are chemically identical. The table does, however, indicate that the colour changes of crustaceans could be brought about by relatively few substances, widely distributed throughout the group.

Name	Principal organ-source	Animal	Effect
A-substance	Sinus glands Post-commissure organs Corpora cardiaca	Natantia Reptantia Brachyura Stomatopoda Insecta	Concentrates red pigments
A′-substance	Post-commissure organs	Isopoda Natantia Stomatopoda	Concentrates white and some red or black pigments
B-substance	Post-commissure organs	Natantia Reptantia (Brachyura?)	Disperses red pigments
Uca-darkening substance	Sinus glands	Natantia Brachyura Limulus	Disperses black pigment

In addition to the above substances there is suggestive evidence for a white pigment disperser and a black pigment concentrator. The evidence for these is less conclusive, possibly because illumination and a rise in temperature seem to have a direct effect on the position of chromatophore pigments and it is therefore difficult to distinguish hormonal effects from the direct effect of the environment in all cases.

Our knowledge of crustacean colour-change was founded on injection and ablation experiments, but there are indications that the limits of these methods have been reached in many cases and that the next advances in the study of crustacean colour change will result from an extension of methods of purification and identification of the chromactivating substances. Extraction and injection experiments have pointed to the possibility that each pigment contained in the various types of crustacean chromatophore may be affected by two substances, one causing dispersal and the other concentration. In assessing these experiments, however, there are various possibilities of error to be borne in mind (Knowles, 1956). The extreme sensitivity of chromatophores to changed conditions of osmotic pressure, concentrations of ions in the blood, etc., and to the artificial introduction of a wide variety of substances into the blood stream, makes the assessment of the results of injection experiments very difficult. There is, moreover, the possibility that injected material may stimulate the release of chromactivators from the injected animal's own neurosecretory system. It is only through the use of purified chromactivating substances that these problems can be resolved.

The wide distribution of the chromactivating substances throughout much of the nervous system in crustaceans (Brown and Saigh, 1946) makes it difficult to apply in crustaceans the classical standards used in vertebrate endocrinology (Kleinholz, 1942), namely that an endocrine effect is conclusively demonstrated only when removal of a suspected organ leads to the display of characteristic symptoms and when injections of extracts or implantations of the suspected organ relieve the symptoms of the deficiency and restore the normal condition. Evidently these standards cannot be applied in the case of, for example, chromactivating hormones which are produced in those neurosecretory cells which extend from the brain along the circumoesophageal connectives to the post-oesophageal commissure and thence to the post-commissure organs (fig. 7). To remove these neurosecretory cells without grave and probably fatal damage to the operated animal would be an impossible task with any known technique.

The lack of ablation experiments has led Kleinholz (1957) to remark that the evidence for a source of chromatophore-activating hormones outside the crustacean eyestalk is not convincing, being adduced predominantly from histological studies and the injection of extracts of central nervous system tissues. We cannot share this view, for in our opinion the future elucidation of the neurosecretory system of crustaceans will depend primarily on the correlation of histological evidence and injection experiments, supplemented by any further evidence that may be available. The ablation of pathways such as those shown in figs. 2 to 10 seems to us to be an impossible task.

The present evidence for the presence of chromactivators outside the crustacean eyestalk is based on the following facts: (1) that the principal regions from which substances concentrating white chromatophore pigments and dispersing red chromatophore pigments can be extracted are the tritocerebral connectives and commissure and the post-commissure organs;

(2) that these substances (which we have named the A'- and B-substances) are not present in any appreciable amount in the eyestalks; (3) that the distribution of the A'- and B-substances corresponds to the distribution of fibres which have particular tinctorial affinities and in which clear evidences of secretion similar to that in the sinus gland can be detected; (4) that animals from which the eyestalks have been removed continue to show colour changes characteristic of the release of A'-substance and B-substance when they are placed in darkness. We consider that these facts, taken together, provide convincing evidence that there is a source of chromatophore-activating hormones outside the crustacean eyestalk, and that it is inter-related evidence of this kind, rather than simple ablation and replacement therapy, which may play an increasingly important part in the study of crustacean neurosecretion. We believe that in the study of neurosecretory systems new standards may have to be devised, and that these will probably rest mainly on the correlation of histologically observable changes to experimentally altered conditions, considered in relation to the identification of active substances in extracts of the suspected secretory tissues and the effects of these substances on target organs. It is evident that the chemical analysis of the chromactivators and other crustacean hormones may play an increasingly important part in the study of crustacean neurosecretion.

It is not surprising that studies on the chemical nature of chromactivating hormones have so far been restricted to those which are chemically most stable and biologically most widely distributed throughout crustaceans—namely the *Uca*-darkening hormone and the *Palaemonetes*-lightening hormones. Owing to the very small amounts of material available, chemical analysis has proved difficult to accomplish. Carlson (1936) was the first to attempt to determine chemical properties of eyestalk extract. He found that an active material would diffuse readily through a cellophane membrane, thus being of relatively low molecular weight; it seems likely that he was studying an α-substance. The material, though soluble in alcohol, was insoluble in ether. Evidently the molecule was a stable one for it could be boiled for a few minutes in dilute HCl or NaOH without losing its effectiveness. Abramowitz (1936a, 1937a, 1938, 1940), in a series of papers, described experiments designed to reveal the nature of the chromactivating substance. He used black chromatophores of the crab *Uca* for assay purposes, and found that the *Uca*-darkening substance which he studied was soluble in alcohol, especially 95 % methyl alcohol, and insoluble in acetone, ether and chloroform. It is interesting to note that the '*Leander*-lightening' substance studied by Östlund and Fänge (1956) appears to be soluble in acetone. It is evident that the solubilities of the *Uca*-darkening and the shrimp-lightening substances are very different.

The most significant evidence so far for the chemical nature of crustacean hormones has been derived from inactivation experiments using tissue extracts or purified enzymes. In 1951 Carstam found that he could inactivate a *Leander*-lightening hormone in eyestalk extracts by incubating them for three hours at 18° C with fragments of the hypodermis of *Leander*, or with extracts of the hepatopancreas of crustaceans or gastropods or the livers of guinea-pigs. The activity of the extracts seemed to be proportional to the concentration and to the time of action on the hormone. He interpreted these results as indicating that the hormone-inactivating substance was an enzyme, but he could not inactivate his eyestalk extracts with the purified enzyme preparations (including proteolytic enzymes) that he employed. It seems likely that his enzymes were inhibited by impurities in the eyestalk extracts, for when we purified our extracts electrophoretically we found that a crystalline preparation of trypsin inactivated the A-substance completely, and that it could also be inactivated by prolonged acid hydrolysis. Östlund and Fänge have recently reported that they have inactivated the shrimp-lightening substance that they have purified by using trypsin and chymo-trypsin, and that the latter is by far the most effective. Pérez González (1957) has reported that it has been possible to inactivate the crab-darkening substance also with chymo-trypsin, and it seems probable that the crustacean chromactivators contain peptide bonds which are essential for their activity. We have found that the A-substance is not inactivated by amino-oxidase or by orthodiphenoloxidase, thus suggesting that it is unlikely that catechol amines are implicated in the activity of the A-substance.

It is possible that the chemical differences between the various crustacean chromactivators may be in some cases relatively slight. This suggestion is supported by the evidence that the A'-substance apparently becomes transformed into the A-substance, and that the A-substance disintegrates to form α-substances. Until the substances are chemically identified this must remain a matter for speculation. There is also room for interesting speculation on the differences between substances which cause dispersal or concentration of the same pigment.

It is interesting to note that the A- and B-substances which have opposite effects on the small red chromatophores of *Leander* also bear opposite electrical charges at pH 7·8; the significance of this is not clear, but it is interesting to speculate whether the configuration of a chromactivating molecule may decide whether or not it is taken into a particular chromatophore and that the charge it bears may determine whether the pigment granules within that chromatophore disperse or concentrate.

RETINAL PIGMENT MOVEMENTS

The crustacean eye has been the object of many anatomical studies. Detailed accounts of its structure have been given by Parker (1897), Kleinholz (1936), Welsh (1930*a*, *b*), Debaisieux (1944), Knowles (1950) and others. The eye is in its general construction similar to the eyes of insects, but the pigments show a greater degree of mobility. We are concerned with these pigment movements, for there is evidence that some of these at least are under hormonal control.

The eye of *Leander serratus*, the common British prawn, comprises some 9000 ommatidia, each of which has the structure shown at fig. 12. Light entering an ommatidium passes first through a biconvex section of the cornea, then through a crystalline cone and finally impinges on a rhabdome, which is surrounded by eight light-sensitive retinal cells. The fibres leading from these cells pass through a fenestrated basement membrane to the lamina ganglionaris, and thence through the three optic ganglia (medulla externa, medulla interna and medulla terminalis) to the brain.

The cornea is faceted in such a way that each ommatidium bears, at its distal end, one facet which is square in surface view and slightly biconvex when viewed in section. Each facet is composed of a thin scaly epicuticle and a thicker cuticle. Two corneal hypodermal cells lie beneath each facet.

The cone consists of four elements which form an elongated

61

pyramid with its square base approximated to the proximal surfaces of the corneal hypodermal cells. In this basal portion there are four nuclei, corresponding to the four elements of the cone. Each cone element is not homogeneous throughout its length, but comprises a cell body, the crystalline cone proper, and an extension which Debaisieux (1944) calls an intermediate crystalline tract. Distally, prolongations of the cone cell bodies appear to pass between the corneal hypodermal cells and may come in contact with the corneal facet. Proximally the intermediate crystalline tract is prolonged into a number (Debaisieux states that there are eleven to the four crystalline tracts in *Palaemon varians*) of fine fibres which extend proximally between the retinular cells and envelop the rhabdome; in some species these fibres extend to the basement membrane, but in *Leander* neither Schneider (1902) nor Trojan (1913) could trace them as far as this.

The cone is surrounded by two pigment cells which have been known variously as 'Hauptpigmentzellen', 'Iris pigment cells', 'Distal retinular cells', and 'Pigmentzellen'. The name 'Distal pigment cell' has been widely adopted in the literature and will be used here. These distal pigment cells contain mainly dark pigment granules, but in addition there is a thin covering sheath of white light-reflecting pigment. The distal and the proximal extensions of the distal pigment cells have been variously described in the literature. Welsh (1930a) depicted a distal extension of the pigment cells to the cornea in *Palaemonetes vulgaris* and a proximal extension by fibres to the distal ends of the retinular cells. Debaisieux (1944) shows a distal extension to form a collar around the corneal hypodermal cells and proximal fibres extending to the basement membrane. In eyes containing both dark and white pigments the connexions are not easily distinguished because the white pigment appears dark by transmitted light and, moreover, it is partly masked by the dark pigment. In preparations of eyes of *Leander serratus* it has been observed (Knowles, 1950) that if the dark pigment is removed by controlled immersion in dilute ammonia, but the white pigment remains, the extensions described by Debaisieux can be seen. If the white pigment only is removed, by immersion in boiling water, the connexions depicted by Welsh can be observed. It appears that the inner darkly pigmented portion of the distal cell is in continuity with the retinular cells proxi-

62

mally and the cornea distally, but the sheath of white pigment is in continuity with the white pigment of the tapetal layer proximally and the cornea hypodermal cells distally.

There are eight proximal retinular cells, though one of these is very reduced in size. Proximally these cells taper to nerve fibres which pass through the basement membrane and gather to form the lamina ganglionaris, whence fibres pass to the medulla externa of the eyestalk. The extensions of the retinular cells between the basement membrane and the lamina ganglionaris are fairly wide, and pigment contained within the retinular cells migrates above or below the basement membrane in response to the illumination falling on the eye. The pigment contained in the retinular cells is known as the proximal pigment.

The tapetal layer comprises a number of nucleated cells, about one to each ten ommatidia, which lie distally to the basement membrane, but with processes extending proximally towards the lamina ganglionaris. The tapetal cells contain a white light-reflecting pigment, and have been compared by Debaisieux to the white chromatophores of the integument; distally they extend to the distal pigment cells and beyond. The pigment they contain is referred to as the reflecting pigment in this account.

The retinal pigments move adaptively after change of illumination (fig. 12). The distal pigment moves proximally in response to illumination and returns to a distal position in darkness or in dim illumination (Kleinholz and Knowles, 1938; Sandeen and Brown, 1952). The proximal pigment migrates below the basement membrane in darkness and distally to it under illumination. The reflecting pigment of *Leander serratus* does not move significantly in response to change of illumination, but that of an allied form, *Palaemonetes vulgaris*, moves proximally when the eye is illuminated and distally when it is not.

The mobility of the retinal pigments is not consistent throughout the Decapoda. At one extreme we find that the proximal pigment only is mobile, for example, in *Penaeus braziliensis*, and that distal and reflecting pigments are fixed in position. At the other extreme there is free mobility of all three pigments, proximal, distal and reflecting as in *Palaemonetes vulgaris*.

THE PROXIMAL PIGMENT. A movement of the proximal pigment seems to be universal among the crustaceans. When the eye is illuminated the greater part of the proximal pigment moves

63

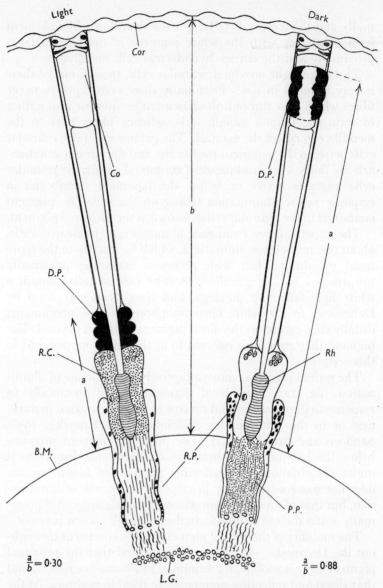

Fig. 12. The position of pigments in a light-adapted crustacean eye contrasted with those in a dark-adapted eye. On the left a single light-adapted ommatidium; on the right a similar ommatidium in darkness. The distances a and b are used to estimate the distal retinal pigment index, which is given as the fraction a/b. *Cor*, cornea; *Co*, cone; *R.C.*, retinular cell; *Rh*, rhabdome; *B.M.*, basement membrane; *L.G.*, lamina ganglionaris; *D.P.*, distal pigment; *P.P.*, proximal pigment; *R.P.*, reflecting pigment.

into that portion of the retinal cell which lies above the basement membrane and thereby screens the photosensitive substances contained within these cells. When dimly illuminated or in darkness the greater part of the proximal pigment moves below the basement membrane thereby exposing the retinal cells to any illumination that there may be.

There is little direct evidence that the movements of the proximal retinal pigment are hormonally controlled, and indeed there is some evidence which seems to point to the contrary. Kleinholz (1949) found that eyes of crayfish isolated from the body and thereby deprived of blood circulation nevertheless showed proximal pigment movements if conditions of illumination were altered. Those experimenters who have exposed one eye of a crustacean to illumination, but have covered the other, have generally found that the proximal pigment of the illuminated eye became light-adapted while that of the darkened eye rested in the dark-adapted condition (Knowles, 1950). This inequality is suggestive evidence that the movement of the proximal pigment is a direct response to illumination, though is not conclusive, for it could be that the response may only be elicited by the combination of a hormone *and* illumination acting simultaneously on the pigment cells. As we shall see presently, there is evidence that illumination appears to sensitize the distal pigment cells to a hormone which influences them. Thus far, however, the only evidence that the movements of the proximal pigment may be influenced by any blood-borne substance has been derived from two isolated injection experiments. In 1939 Welsh brought about a light adaptation of the proximal pigment in *Cambarus* in darkness by injection of an eyestalk extract. This has been repeated in *Penaeus braziliensis* (Knowles, unpublished), but most investigators have not been able to detect any change in the position of the proximal pigment in other species after injections of eyestalk extract, and it seems possible that the effects obtained after injection of *Cambarus* and *Penaeus* might have been due to an induced hypoxaemia, which is known to bring about light adaptation of the proximal pigment in darkness. To sum up, though there is insufficient evidence to enable us to avow with confidence that movements of the proximal retinal pigment are not under hormonal control, such evidence as we have does not favour this possibility.

THE DISTAL PIGMENT. There is abundant evidence, on the

other hand, that movement of the distal retinal pigment is under the control of a hormone released by the sinus gland. The first indication of this was given by Kleinholz (1936), who brought about light adaptation of the distal pigment in darkened specimens of *Palaemonetes vulgaris* by injecting them with an eyestalk extract; the degree of migration was proportional to the dose. Removal of the sinus glands without blinding led to an immobility of the distal pigment in *Leander* (Knowles, 1950), which remained in a dark-adapted condition under all conditions of illumination after the operation. Welsh (1941) found that aqueous extracts of isolated sinus glands would, on injection, bring about typical migration of the retinal pigments of the crayfish.

We have as yet little information about the substance which promotes light adaptation of the distal retinal pigment, beyond the fact that it seems to be released by the sinus gland when the eye is illuminated. The results of injection experiments have indicated that it is present in greater amounts under illumination than in darkness (Kleinholz, 1936), but Brown and his collaborators have suggested that there is a storage of light-adapting hormone in darkness. Their reasoning is based on the greater amount of light adaptation invoked by a brief flash if an animal has been for many hours in darkness than if it has recently been placed in darkness. This apparent contradiction between the experiments of Kleinholz and Brown could be explained by the supposition that a greater amount of light-adapting hormone is produced and released during illumination of the animal than in darkness, but that during prolonged exposure to darkness the relatively small amount of hormone that is present tends to accumulate at the terminations of the neurosecretory fibres in a form which can be immediately released if the animal's photoreceptors are stimulated.

It has not yet been ascertained with complete certainty whether the distal retinal pigment hormone is distinct from the chromactivating hormones known to be present in the sinus gland though there is evidence which favours a distinct retinal pigment hormone. The coincidence of light adaptation of the distal retinal pigment with dark adaptation of the dark chromatophore pigments when a shrimp is placed on an illuminated black background would suggest that there is a distinct distal pigment hormone. A final resolution of the problem can only be achieved by the purification of the chromactivating principles, and the subsequent testing of their effects on the distal retinal pigment. We (Kleinholz, Knowles, Carlisle, unpublished) have found by injection experiments that purified preparations of the A-substance isolated from sinus glands by us, using paper electrophoresis, the substance isolated from *Pandalus* by Östlund and Fänge (1956), and material from *Bombyx* heads supplied to us by Dr Peter Karlson, are without effect on the distal retinal pigment of *Leander serratus* kept in darkness, although these extracts had a typical and strong effect on the chromatophore pigments. We have not yet been able to separate a substance which affects retinal pigments but not chromatophore pigments though some experimental results give us reason to hope that this may be possible. Certainly whole eyestalk extracts affect both retinal and chromatophore pigments, and it has been possible to separate substances with chromatophore effect only; these results, taken together, indicate a separate retinal pigment hormone.

The hormonal control of light adaptation of the distal pigment is evident, but the mechanism of distal pigment dark adaptation is less clear, though studies by Brown and his collaborators have indicated the possibility of a 'dark-adapting' hormone for the distal retinal pigment. Their reasoning is based on the behaviour of the distal retinal pigment in *Palaemonetes* in darkness, following a brief exposure to a powerful light flash (250 foot-candles for one minute). This seems to be sufficient stimulus to bring about a light adaptation, the degree of which varied with the pretreatment of the animals; the greatest degree of light adaptation was found in those animals which had been longest in darkness before the flash, and Brown and his collaborators have interpreted this as due to a storage of the light-adapting hormone in darkness. One might have expected that the greater the degree of light adaptation in these experiments the longer would have been the return to the previously dark-adapted position. It is certainly true of injection experiments involving chromatophore pigment movements that the duration of a response is broadly proportional to the concentration of the activating hormone, and Kleinholz found that this was so also in his experiments on the distal retinal pigment. Surprisingly, however, Brown, Hines and Fingerman (1952) found that when light adaptation of the distal pigment was provoked in darkness by

67   5-2

means of a brief flash, the longer the period in darkness the longer the period of light adaptation of the distal pigment, but also the more rapid the subsequent period of dark adaptation. Brown and his collaborators have interpreted these results as indicating the storage of a dark-adapting hormone also.

Injection experiments to support the thesis of a dark-adapting hormone for the distal pigment have not yet yielded conclusive results, inasmuch as no injected extract has yet brought about a dark adaptation of the distal pigment in an illuminated eye. It is, however, possible that illumination may destroy a dark-adapting hormone, or minimize its effect. It must also be noted that the experiments which have so far been designed to evoke dark adaptation of the distal pigment by injections have been carried out at intensities of illumination which produced complete light adaptation of the eye, and the injected material had therefore to compete with a maximal titre of light-adapting hormone. When, however, an injection of an extract of trito-cerebral commissure material was given simultaneously with exposure to a flash in darkness, the degree of light adaptation was less than if no injection had been given. This is suggestive evidence that there is in the commissure region a substance which antagonizes the effect of the sinus gland distal pigment light-adapting hormone. If this can be substantiated more fully, it would provide an interesting parallel to the known antagonism of the small-red-chromatophore-activating hormones of the sinus gland and the post-commissure organs.

THE REFLECTING PIGMENT. There is some evidence that the movements of the reflecting pigment are under hormonal control. Debaisieux (1944) has pointed to a general resemblance between the reflecting pigment cells and the white chromatophores of the integument. In those crustacean eyes in which the reflecting pigment is mobile, light adaptation is brought about by a migration of a proportion of the white pigment into the processes which lie beneath the basement membrane. If we may pursue the comparison with chromatophores, this would correspond to a pigment dispersal, similar to that which takes place in the white chromatophores when they are exposed to illumination. Conversely in darkness the retinal reflecting pigment concentrates in that portion of the cell which lies between the retinular cells; this would correspond to the concentration of the pigments of the white chromatophores in darkness.

The movements of the distal pigment are clearly defined and may be estimated quantitatively by measurement. Those of the reflecting pigment, however, involve the shift of a proportion of the pigment only, and so quantitative estimation is difficult. In 1936 Kleinholz reported that injections of whole eyestalk extracts into normal individuals of *Palaemonetes* in darkness brought about a movement of the reflecting pigment towards the light-adapted position. On the other hand, in *Leander serratus* no significant difference between the position of the reflecting pigment in the eyes of normal animals and of that in the eyes of operated animals from which the sinus glands had been removed could be detected (Knowles, 1950). The reflecting pigment of *Leander serratus* is, however, considerably less mobile than that of *Palaemonetes*, and the observations on the reflecting pigment of *Leander* were not made on a sufficiently large number of animals to enable conclusive results to be drawn. In view of the apparent similarity between the reflecting pigment cells and the white chromatophores of the integument it would be interesting to discover whether the injection of an extract containing a white-pigment-concentrating hormone (A'-substance) would promote dark-adaptation of the reflecting pigment of an illuminated animal. If so, the apparent contradiction between the injection and ablation experiments reported above might be resolved, and the post-commissure organs indicated as a source of a hormone controlling the reflecting retinal pigment movements.

CHAPTER 4

The Pericardial Organs and Heart Beat

THE pericardial organs, discovered by Alexandrowicz (1952-3), are neurohaemal organs lying within the pericardial cavity and bathed freely by blood which is moving towards the heart. First described in *Squilla*, under the name of dorsal lamellae, they have since been found in all groups of Malacostraca examined by Alexandrowicz. Each consists of nerve fibres ending in a branching network, which, with some connective tissues, forms a neuropile-like structure. No nerve cell bodies have been seen in these organs and the nerve cells which supply them have not been traced. The dorsal lamellae of *Squilla* lie free within the pericardium stretching from one side to the other, spanning the whole cavity. Another part of the system of pericardial organs is spread out over the wall of the pericardium with the ramifying endings exposed to the blood stream (cf. the post-commissure organs, p. 25). Essentially the same condition is found in *Homarus* and *Leander*, with part stretching across the pericardium and part spread over the wall; in *Penaeus* the latter part is much more prominent. In crabs the pericardial organs are composed of thick nervous trunks, consisting of nerve fibres surrounded by the neuropile-like network, lying on the inside of the lateral pericardial wall in such a position that their stoutest parts span the three openings of the branchio-cardiac veins. Whatever the detailed arrangement of the pericardial organs, they are always so placed that the blood coming to the pericardium from the gills passes immediately over them. And the evidence suggests that they release into this blood hormones which regulate the amplitude and rate of the heart beat.

Within the pericardial organs, Alexandrowicz could see no granules or droplets which he could not interpret as artifacts; his observations were made with the light microscope. In electron microscope studies performed by Dr D. Maynard, in the Harvard Biological Laboratories under the direction of Professor J. H. Welsh (unpublished), granules have been demonstrated in the pericardial organs of the crab *Carcinus* about 1200 Å in diameter (and therefore below the limit of resolution of the light microscope). These granules probably represent the stored hormonal material. Electron microscope studies on the pericardial organs of the Stomatopod *Squilla mantis* have also demonstrated granules approximately 1200 Å in diameter (Plate III). It is interesting to note the similarity in size of the pericardial granules in two such unlike crustaceans.

The influence of the pericardial organs on the heart beat has been investigated by Alexandrowicz and Carlisle (1953).

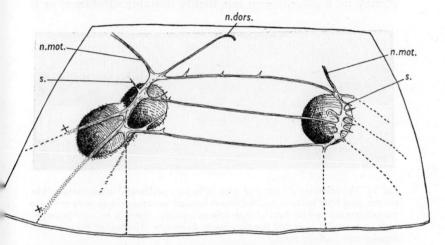

Fig. 13. Semidiagrammatic view of the pericardial organs of the right side of *Maia squinado*. The organs are shown in place on the inside of the lateral pericardial wall with the openings of the three branchio-cardiac veins. The nerves running from the central nervous system into the pericardial organs are drawn by dotted lines. The points at which the two anterior nerves pass into prolongations of the bar which is situated in the lumen of the vein are indicated by crosses. *n.mot.*, nerves running to the muscles; *n.dors.*, dorsal nerve of the heart; *s.*, strands suspending the trunks. (Reprinted from Alexandrowicz, 1953*a*.)

Extracts of pericardial organs of various species of decapods and stomatopods had the same effects on the heart beat, when tested on any one species, though the response differed in different species. The amplitude of beat was always increased; but in some species the frequency increased, while in others it decreased after perfusion of the isolated heart with extract of pericardial organs. As little as one hundredth part of the extract obtained from the pericardial organs of one animal sometimes produced an effect. The heart beat of Crustacea is affected by adrenalin, noradrenalin and acetylcholine in low concentration, but in ways unlike the action of the pericardial organ extract. The action of 5-hydroxytryptamine, however, is almost indistinguishable from that of the extract. Paper chromatography of the extracts reveals two active spots, neither of which is 5-hydroxytryptamine, but one of them is clearly closely related. Carlisle (1956 b) has shown that this substance is an *ortho*dihydroxyindole alkylamine, and it is likely that it is in fact 5,6-dihydroxytryptamine. The other active substance remains unidentified. It may be a precursor of this highly unstable substance, or it

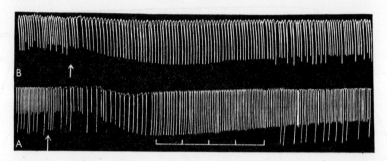

Fig. 14. The effect on the heart of *Maia* of its own pericardial organ extract. The records read from left to right; the arrows indicate the approximate time at which the extracts reached the hearts; time scale in minutes. Note the increase in amplitude, the steadier beat and the decrease in frequency. (Reprinted from Alexandrowicz and Carlisle, 1953.)

may be, as Professor Welsh has suggested (personal communication) a polypeptide, quite unrelated to the first substance. A comparable situation is seen in vertebrates in the action on blood pressure of 5-hydroxytryptamine and that of the polypeptide, substance P (Östlund and von Euler, 1957).

The naturally occurring substance in the pericardial organs has been detected in the blood. Addition of sodium hydroxide in high concentration followed by brisk aeration yields a characteristic evanescent fluorescence with the active extracts of pericardial organs. This reaction is given by blood which is taken from the pericardium, that is, blood which has passed over the pericardial organs but which has not yet reached the heart, while it is absent from blood which has once passed through the heart. Presumably it is removed from the blood by the heart which is thus caused to respond. When the excised pericardial organs are placed in a saline bath and one of the nerves leading to them is stimulated, the active substance is released into the saline.

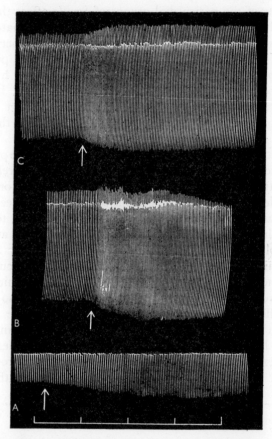

Fig. 15. The effect on the heart of *Homarus* of (A) pericardial organ extract of *Homarus*, (B) pericardial organ extract of *Cancer*, and (C) pericardial organ extract of *Maia*. Records read from left to right; the arrows indicate approximately the time at which the extracts reached the heart; time scale in minutes. Note that in this species the extracts induce an increase in frequency of heart beat. (Reprinted from Alexandrowicz and Carlisle, 1953.)

The substances stored in the pericardial organs, then, are necessary for the proper functioning of the heart, released into the blood by the organs and discharged as a result of nervous stimulation. We have no information on the effects of extirpation of the organs—the operation seems at present impossible. But even in the absence of such knowledge it seems safe to conclude that the pericardial organ is in fact engaged in the release of hormones which regulate the heart beat.

Extracts of the pericardial organs of *Squilla* affect the heart beat without having any influence on the chromatophores (Knowles and Carlisle, 1956), while extracts of the pericardial organs of *Maia* may provoke concentration of the red pigments of *Leander*; 5-hydroxytryptamine and a mixture of hydroxylated products prepared from this compound, and believed to contain 5, 6-dihydroxytryptamine, had no effect on the chromatophores of *Leander*, but strongly stimulated the heart beat.

The rate of heart beat and degree of dispersion of the pigments of the red chromatophores are, however, often correlated in many natural and experimental conditions. Reported originally by Keeble and Gamble (1900), this correlation has been sometimes considered close enough (e.g. by Brown, 1944) to justify the conclusion that the chromactivating substance and that responsible for accelerating the heart beat were one and the same. This now seems unlikely, for Welsh (1939), Scudamore (1941) and Hara (1952 a, b) have prepared extracts which affect both the red chromatophores and the heart beat, but also extracts which affect only the red chromatophores and are without action on the heart beat, while Hara has prepared an extract affecting heart beat but not the chromatophores. When boiled eyestalk extracts of *Leander* have been subjected to electrophoresis on paper the substance responsible for accelerating the heart

---

LEGEND TO PLATE IV

(1) Pericardial organs of the left side of *Maia squinado*. Parts of the pericardium are still attached to the trunks.

(2) Posterior part of the pericardial organs of *Maia squinado*.

(3) Part of the posterior bar of the pericardial organs of *Maia squinado*, showing the intermingling of nerve fibres coming from various directions. The nerve fibres are surrounded by the neuropile-like structure, represented in this preparation by the dots (artifacts from methylene blue staining) which delimit the structure.

(4) Anterior portion of the pericardial organs of the right side of *Cancer pagurus*. The trunks span the second opening of the branchio-cardiac veins. Note the absence of the neuropile-like sheaths in the lower parts of the trunks. These parts are embedded in the tissue of the pericardium and not exposed to the blood stream.

These photomicrographs, reprinted from Alexandrowicz (1953a), were all taken from preparations stained with methylene blue.

PLATE IV

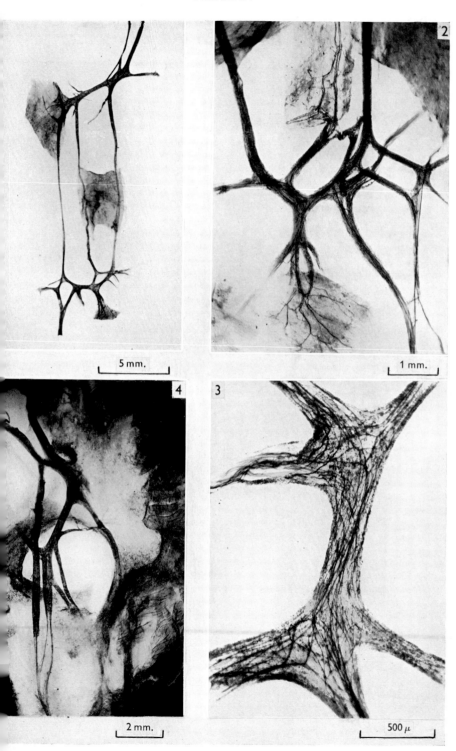

5 mm.

1 mm.

2 mm.

500 μ

beat has been separated from the chromactivating substances (Carlisle, unpublished). It seems to be a polypeptide.

It appears, then, that the substances responsible for stimulating the heart beat and those for regulating the chromatophores are distinct, for extracts have been prepared which affect the one but are without influence on the other. Until, however, the chromactivating principle of the sinus gland has been obtained in pure form it will not be possible to state with certainty that it is without effect on the heart; nor conversely can it be stated that the heart-beat-regulating substances are without effect on the chromatophores. Undoubtedly the control of the chromatophores and the regulation of the heart beat are closely associated in the natural state, and environmental conditions of illumination and background modify the state of expansion of the chromatophores and the rate of heart beat simultaneously. But whereas the major centres of control of the chromatophores appear to be the X organ-sinus gland complex and the post-commissure organs, there is little doubt that the pericardial organs are the main crustacean organs for the regulation of the heart beat.

CHAPTER 5

Growth, Moulting, Development and Metabolism

GROWTH AND MOULTING

In Crustaceans, as in insects, the processes of growth can be distinguished from mere increase in size. A crustacean increases in size by a succession of moults (though moulting may take place without any increase in size, or, indeed, with an actual decrease). At each normal moult the old shell is cast and the animal swells by the absorption of water—often by actual drinking. The outer layers of the skin are then hardened as the new shell, one size larger. This increase in size at moulting, then, is merely an increase in the wet weight of the body. Throughout the rest of the intermoult period, before the next moult, the water is gradually replaced by new tissue, either by the swelling of old cells or by the formation of new ones; at all events the amount of protein in the body increases and the amount of water decreases. In our view this replacement of water by new tissue (involving protein synthesis and mitoses) is the true growth.

The metabolism of Crustacea, then, is notable for the markedly cyclical nature of the physiological processes of growth, constrained as this is by the necessity for frequent moults. And so closely interlocked and interdependent are these cyclical changes that experimental interference with one inevitably leads to other metabolic effects. Thus eyestalk removal may lead to an increase in ovarian weight, to an upset of water balance, to an altered rate of moulting, to a different oxygen consumption and to a modified R.Q. In this account, therefore, we intend to give an overall picture of the main processes of growth and moulting and of phenomena associated with them, without trying to determine whether distinct effects are the result of the action of one or many hormones, except where the evidence is rather clear on this point. But first a detailed consideration of the moult cycle is necessary (see fig. 16). For practical purposes the scheme of division of the moult cycle proposed by Drach (1939) is the most convenient, but certain theoretical considerations not apparent in his scheme make that of Carlisle and Dohrn (1952) more suitable for purposes of discussion. In this scheme the moult cycle is divided into the following stages:

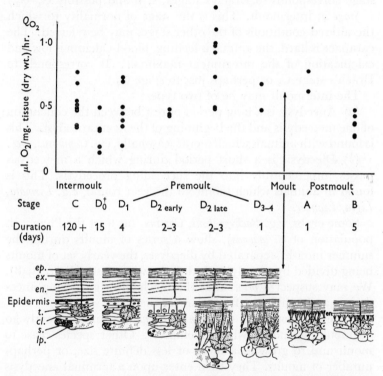

Fig. 16. The structure and metabolism of the integumentary tissue of *Gecarcinus lateralis* at each stage of the moult cycle. Each point on the graph represents the Q_{O_2} of tissue from a crab in the stage of the moult cycle sketched below. Q_{O_2} determined by Warburg method. Reproduced by permission of Dr Dorothy Skinner. *cl.* = cell of Leydig; *en.* = endocuticle; *ep.* = epicuticle; *ex.* = exocuticle; *lp.* = lipoprotein cell; *s.* = blood sinus; *t.* = tegumental gland.

Stage 1: proecdysis or premoult. During this stage the animal is preparing to moult, most noticeably by the removal of calcium from the exoskeleton, which becomes brittle and may flake off in the more highly calcified forms. With this is correlated a rise in the blood-calcium level. (This corresponds to Drach's stage D.)

77

Stage 2: ecdysis, moult or exuviation. This is the short period of the cycle while the animal is actually shedding its exoskeleton.

Stage 3: metecdysis or postmoult. This is the period when the new exoskeleton is hardening and the animal is returning to normal in its physiological condition; it is still not yet feeding, and in its behaviour tends to shun the more exposed positions. (This stage corresponds to Drach's stages A, B and possibly C_1–C_3.)

Stage 4: intermoult. This is the stage of normality to which the altered conditions of the other stages may be referred. The carapace is hard, the animal is feeding, blood-calcium is low and calcification of the integument maximal. (It corresponds to Drach's stage C, or perhaps just to stage C_4.)

The intermoult may be of two types:

(*a*) Anecdysis is a long period of rest between the conclusion of one metecdysis and the beginning of the next proecdysis. This is found with animals which moult seasonally, e.g. *Cambarus, Uca*.

(*b*) Diecdysis is a short period during which a metecdysis passes imperceptibly into the succeeding proecdysis. This is found in animals which moult all the year round, e.g. *Lysmata, Ligia, Leander*.

Some crabs, e.g. *Pachygrapsus, Carcinus* (at least the Plymouth population of *C. maenas*), show a series of moults during the summer months, separated by diecdyses, the yearly set of moults being divided by anecdyses during the winter (see Hiatt, 1948). We may suspect *a priori* that the mechanism governing anecdysis may be different from that for diecdysis.

Some decapods, e.g. *Cancer* and *Homarus*, can apparently go on moulting and growing indefinitely. Other species cease to moult and to grow at a more or less definite size, or perhaps number of moults. They then enter upon a terminal anecdysis and never, except after experimental interference, enter upon another proecdysis as long as they may live. *Pachygrapsus, Leander, Carcinus, Maia, Portunus* and *Callinectes* seem to fall into this class.

Nothing is known of the endocrinology of moulting before metamorphosis, and the life history may follow several different lines after this takes place. It is of course obvious that all major changes in the anatomy of the animal must take place at a moult. The copulatory appendages for instance can only appear at a moult when the old shell, which lacks them, is cast and the new shell develops with them. Certain moults, therefore, are critical to the development of the animal and are unlike other moults. The most spectacular of these are those of metamorphosis, but the moults of prepuberty and puberty are equally of importance. A brief summary of the life history, in terms of moults, of a few species of decapods after metamorphosis may prove useful here.

(*a*) In *Carcinus*, several moults after metamorphosis, occurs the moult of puberty (there is probably a prepuberal moult, but this is not established for sure). At this moult the copulatory appendages first appear and the animals become sexually mature and able to reproduce. The crabs are then about 16 mm. across the carapace. Ten or eleven moults and three years later they undergo the last moult and enter upon the terminal anecdysis, never to moult again. The largest males have a carapace breadth (in the Plymouth population—other populations differ) of 86 mm.; the females are smaller.

(*b*) In *Maia* the animals are already quite large when they undergo the prepuberal moult. At this moult the increase in size is greater than at other moults and the sexes first become externally different. Three moults later they undergo the final moult which is also the moult of puberty; they never moult again once sexually mature. The last few moults take place only in July or August.

(*c*) In *Leander* nothing is known of any prepuberal moult and the moult of puberty takes place when the prawn is rather small. Thereafter it may moult an indefinite number of times until a limiting size is reached, whereupon it is unlikely to moult again, or, if it should, it does not increase in size at this moult. The females are larger than the males. The interval between moults depends upon the temperature and the size.

(*d*) In *Lysmata* the moult of prepuberty takes place at about 10–12 mm. length and that of puberty about five to seven moults and six months later, when each individual becomes a male. Ten moults and eighteen months later the critical moult occurs, when the male copulatory appendages are shed and the opening of the vas deferens is sealed by the new shell. Depending on the state of nutrition of the individual this same moult may result in a sterile intersex, if food reserves are low, or if they are high the new shell may have at once all the characteristics of the female so that the animal can copulate at once as a female. At least twelve more moults may take place after this critical moult

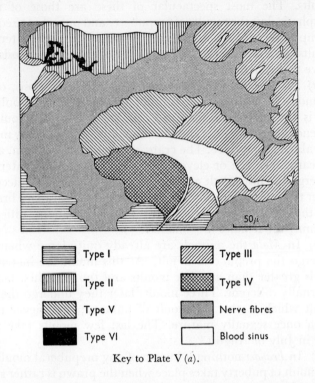

Key to Plate V (a).

and the animal may remain as a sexless individual for up to three intermoults. The life history of *Pandalus* is similar.

The influence of the eyestalks on moulting has been known for over fifty years and it is nearly twenty years since it was first suggested that this influence was hormonal. Removal of the eyestalks from a decapod during the intermoult period usually results in the initiation of the processes of proecdysis and hence causes the animal to moult after a period. Drach (1944) and Guyselman (1953) showed that eyestalk removal did not hasten moulting if performed when the animal had already begun proecdysis. The effect of eyestalk ablation, in this respect, is to trigger the beginning of the premoult. It was already known from the work of Kyer (1942) and Scudamore (1942, 1947) that the onset of premoult and the subsequent moult could be delayed after eyestalk removal by implantation of sinus glands, and all the metabolic changes which resulted in eyestalk removal could

PLATE V

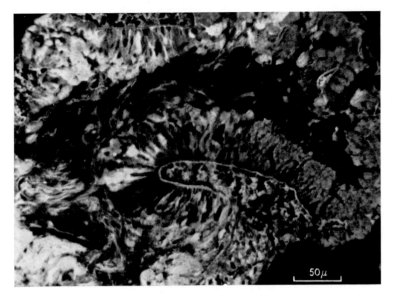

a

(*a*) The sinus gland of *Callinectes sapidus* showing the distribution of the six types of tinctorially distinct neurosecretory nerve endings—see key on facing page.

(Photograph supplied by Dr David Potter of the Department of Biophysics, University College, London.)

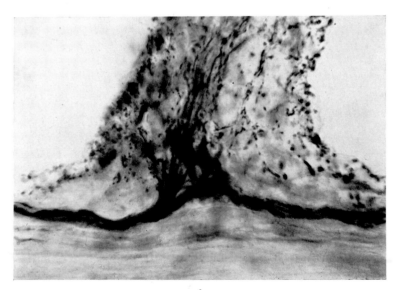

b

(*b*) The base of a post-commissure organ stained with methylene blue. Only neurosecretory fibres are stained. The fine droplets probably represent secretory material, distorted by fixation or staining (× 350).

be, at least partially, abolished. Then, independently, Bliss (1951, 1953) and Passano (1951a, 1953) found that removal of the sinus gland alone had no effect on the moulting, though they confirmed that eyestalk removal under their particular conditions of experiment did in fact precipitate proecdysis. The sinus gland, then, contained the principle responsible for preventing the premature start of proecdysis, but its removal was not sufficient stimulus for proecdysis to begin. Passano (1953) solved this enigma by showing that the effects of bilateral eyestalk removal could be duplicated by removal of not just the sinus glands alone, but these together with the group of neurosecretory cells which chiefly supply them—the medulla terminalis ganglionic X organ. Conversely, if these two organs were implanted together, with their anatomical connexions intact, into animals whose eyestalks had been removed, all precocious moulting was inhibited, whereas either organ implanted separately, or together with the connexions severed, only partially inhibited precocious moulting. His experiments suggested that a moult-inhibiting hormone is produced by cells of the ganglionic X organ and transported along the axons of the X organ-sinus gland tract to the sinus gland where it is stored and finally released. He regarded the sinus gland as no more than a reservoir of the hormone, not a centre of production. He showed that the hormone may be produced in neurosecretory cells in other parts of the central nervous system, but that it is probably released chiefly at the sinus gland. This view now has the support of most workers in the field of crustacean endocrinology.

The X organ-sinus gland complex has been shown to secrete a moult-inhibiting hormone in all Malacostraca in which it has been sought. This hormone serves to inhibit the onset of proecdysis and of all the concomitant processes, such as laying down calcium and food reserves. The hormone has also been found in neurosecretory centres of the brain and central nervous system.

Once proecdysis has begun the moult-inhibiting hormone is without effect and the processes of the premoult are regulated by another hormone which has been called the moult-accelerating hormone, because its most noticeable effect is to speed proecdysis. This hormone is without known effect in any stage of the moult cycle except proecdysis. It is secreted by neurosecretory cell groups in the brain and central nervous system and also, in those animals which have a well-developed sensory pore X organ, by the cells of the medulla terminalis ganglionic X organ. In the eyestalk, the hormone appears to be transported from these cells to the sensory pore X organ, where it is stored and finally released (Carlisle and Dohrn, 1952, 1953; Carlisle, 1953*c*). In those groups of decapods in which the sensory pore X organ is reduced or absent—the Astacura and the Brachyura—the hormone is absent from the eyestalk. In these groups, therefore, experiments on the influence of the eyestalk on the incidence of moulting are relatively uncomplicated since there appears to be only the moult-inhibiting hormone which might affect the rate. In such an animal as *Leander* in which the eyestalks secrete both a moult-inhibiting and a moult-accelerating hormone, apparently contradictory results may be obtained. Thus Drach (1944) found that eyestalk ablation led to a decreased inter-moult period, while we have found this operation led to a lengthened intermoult period (Carlisle, 1953*f*). Drach and ourselves used populations of prawns which differ both ana-tomically (Carlisle, 1955) and in the moult rate under identical conditions. Using the same population as Drach, we have been able to confirm his results, while at the same time confirming our own quite contradictory results with another population. In more detailed study it has become apparent that eyestalk removal leads to a quicker onset of proecdysis, but that this pro-cess is slower in completion. If the quicker onset is exactly balanced by the delay in proecdysis, then the overall effect will be no change in the moult rate after eyestalk removal—as, indeed, Scheer and Scheer (1954*a*, *b*), in yet another population of the same species, have found. If, however, the two effects are not balanced, then the overall effect of eyestalk removal on the rate of moulting may be either an increase or a decrease.

The duration of anecdysis, then, is controlled by the secretion of a hormone which inhibits the beginning of proecdysis. The course of proecdysis, once begun, is regulated by the moult-accelerating hormone. Ecdysis itself is to some extent also regulated by a hormone of the X organ-sinus gland complex. This is the water-balance-regulating hormone which, among other functions, controls the uptake of water at ecdysis.

At first sight it might appear that these three hormones, so far as they concern growth and moulting, are morphogenetic hormones. Recent work by Gabe and Echalier, however, makes it likely that the moult-inhibiting and the moult-accelerating

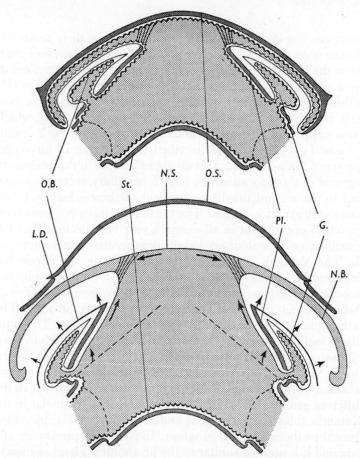

Fig. 17. Moulting in *Maia squinado*. Diagrammatic transverse sections through the middle region of the cephalothorax just before moulting begins (upper), and during moulting (lower). In the earlier of these two stages the old shell and the new integument are everywhere separated and the new integument is pleated. Imbibition of water causes an increased volume within the new integument, which stretches to accommodate it. The result of the first stage of this stretching is illustrated in the lower diagram where the rigid curved shell is pushed off the back as the new integument takes up a curve with a greater radius of curvature. This involves the shell's cracking along the line of dehiscence (*L.D.*). Muscles, whose only function lies in the act of moulting and are never used at any other time, assist the process of withdrawal from the shell; a pair of the more important ones is indicated in the dorsal region. The expansion of the dorsal integument takes place before that of the ventral, resulting in a pivoting action along the line of the gills; this is indicated by the arrows and the pecked lines radiating upwards from the gills: above these lines the first movement takes place, below these lines there is no expansion until the next stage of the moulting. *G.*, gills; *L.D.*, line of dehiscence; *N.B.*, new roof of the branchial chamber; *N.S.*, new integument; *O.B.*, old roof of the branchial chamber; *O.S.*, old shell; *Pl.*, pleural plate; *St.*, sternum. (Redrawn, with modifications, after Drach, 1939.)

hormones are endocrinokinetic; that is to say, their main influence is on another endocrine gland as an effector rather than upon the morphogenetic processes directly. The effector organ upon which they apparently act is the Y organ of Gabe (1953 *b*). If this organ is removed, eyestalk ablation and injection of eyestalk extracts have no effect whatsoever upon moulting, which cannot apparently take place at all in the absence of the Y organ.

Gabe (1953, 1956) has described the Y organ in fifty-eight species of Malacostraca. It is an organ located in the antennary segment of those forms which have a maxillary excretory organ and in the second maxillary segment of those which have an antennary excretory organ. The crustacean larva possesses both excretory organs, but in all except a very few species either the maxillary or the antennary kidney degenerates at metamorphosis. The Y organ is found in the place of the one which has degenerated in the adult, but it is not developed from the degenerated organ and it is found also in those species (e.g. *Nebalia*) which retain both excretory organs into the adult. The cells, equal in size, have an average diameter of 10μ. The cytoplasm lacks glycogen and osmophilic lipoids, but is rich in ribonucleates and in alkaline phosphatases. It is not, except in the Brachyura where it is relatively large, especially vascularized and it lacks a secretory canal. Macroscopically it varies in form in the different groups; it is conical in the Brachyura, lenticular in the Natantia, foliaceous in Isopoda and Amphipoda. It is innervated from the suboesophageal ganglion. In position, appearance and function it is notably similar to the prothoracic gland of insects.

Echalier (1954, 1955) has shown that bilateral ablation of the Y organ in *Carcinus* during anecdysis, diecdysis or early proecdysis completely prevents any start of proecdysis or its further progress if started. If the operation is performed during late proecdysis, the animal proceeds to moult and continues to the next anecdysis where it remains, never moulting again. Implantation of Y organ tissue allows the moult cycle to start again. Eyestalk ablation or injection of eyestalk extracts has no influence at all on the moulting of crabs from which the Y organs have been removed. It seems probable that the moult-inhibiting and the moult-accelerating hormones of the eyestalk exert their influence *via* the Y organ, which itself is the main secretor of the morphogenetic hormones concerned with growth and moulting. If further research confirms this hypothesis, it will be seen that the moult cycle of crustaceans is under a chain of control very like that of the insects. Indeed, Karlson (1956) has purified from *Crangon* a substance similar to ecdysone of insects. He, Skinner and Carlisle (unpublished) have found that the insect hormone is active on crustaceans and that the crustacean hormone promotes moulting in insects.

The total increase in volume which commonly takes place at moulting is a result of absorption of water through the integument and gills. The swelling which is thus brought about may play a large part in opening up the old shell along the lines of dehiscence and hence be of importance in the actual mechanics of the moult process (see fig. 17). Removal of the eyestalks in crabs and crayfish has been shown to lead to a greater increase in volume at each moult. Koch (1952) showed that this greater increase of volume is not a result of greater formation of tissue during the premoult, but simply due to a disturbed water metabolism. If the eyestalks are removed from crabs one to three days before moulting, and the crabs are starved thereafter, the increase in volume at moulting is far greater than normal; this of course cannot be due to a greater formation of tissue, but must be a result of disturbed water balance (Carlisle, unpublished).

Implantation or injection of sinus glands or extracts partially or wholly prevents the greater uptake of water in eyestalkless animals at moulting. The sinus gland thus contains the hormone responsible for the regulation of this function. But Bliss (1953) has shown that it is not produced here, and that the gland serves only as a release centre. It has been suggested that the effects on water balance of eyestalk removal and of injection of eyestalk extracts are only further manifestations of the moult-inhibiting hormone, but recent evidence suggests that this is not so. The water-balance-regulating hormone seems to be distinct from the moult-inhibiting hormone.

We have found that in *Carcinus* after eyestalk ablation not only is more water taken up—about 180 % of the premoult body volume instead of the normal 80 %—but it is taken up more quickly. The effect can be counteracted by injection of eyestalk extract or of sinus-gland extract, and if either of these extracts is injected into an intact crab less water than usual is taken up in a longer time, so that the moult process takes an inordinately long time. The principle which has this effect is found in both the sinus gland and the *M.T.G.X.* (Carlisle, 1956a).

The great increase in water intake which follows eyestalk removal may continue for moult after moult. But as the interval between moults is certainly no longer than usual and may be shorter, not all this excess water can be replaced by tissue in the intermoult period. Thus the percentage of water in the tissues is greater after each successive moult. In the absence of suitable injections we have found it impossible to keep *Leander* or *Carcinus* for more than about six or seven moults after eyestalk ablation. Death of these experimental animals, which usually takes place at a little before moulting, seems to be a consequence of too great a dilution of the tissues, so that the animal dies, as it were, of overdrinking (Carlisle, unpublished).

It is possible to prepare eyestalk extracts, from suitable donors, which affect the water balance without at the same time inhibiting the onset of proecdysis. The reverse has not so far proved possible, but it seems unlikely that the two effects are the results of the activity of one and the same hormone.

Eyestalk ablation and injection of eyestalk extracts lead to alterations of the water balance at any stage in the moult cycle, and not only at the moult itself. Eyestalk ablation enables the animal to withstand lower salinities, while injection of eyestalk extracts raises the tolerance to heightened salinities (Carlisle, 1956a). Just as in vertebrates, there is a diurnal rhythm of water uptake in crabs throughout the moult cycle (Guyselman, 1953), and this appears once more to be regulated by the X organ-sinus gland complex. Probably it is one more manifestation of the hormone which regulates water balance and diuresis.

The X organ-sinus gland complex of the eyestalk thus exerts control over the moult cycle through three distinct hormones— the moult-inhibiting hormone, which regulates the length of anecdysis, the moult-accelerating hormone, which regulates proecdysis, and the water-balance-regulating hormone, which controls increase in size at moulting. Nothing is known of any control of metecdysis, and diecdysis does not appear to be regulated by the moult-inhibiting hormone in the same way as anecdysis. There is thus a large gap in our knowledge of the endocrinology of moulting covering these two stages of the moult cycle.

Before we turn from the normal moult to the special moults, such as that of puberty and the final moult, it would be well to consider some of the metabolic processes which change throughout the moult cycle and which appear to be under hormonal control. Since these changes are so closely associated with the moult cycle, it may seem probable that their control is by means of the same hormones which regulate the moult cycle, but there is no guarantee of this and we have not the information available to decide the question.

SUGAR, GLYCOGEN AND CHITIN. Since chitin consists, at least in part, of a chain of glucosamine molecules the relation between sugar and chitin, and hence between sugar and moulting, is obvious. Some of the glucose present in the blood during metecdysis is used to form glucosamine and chitin for the reproduction of the new shell.

Rather indirect evidence suggests the existence of a mechanism which keeps the level of sugar in the blood down below a maximum, acting like insulin in vertebrates, but it is not even known (though suspected) that this mechanism is hormonal. There is rather clearer evidence for the existence of an endocrine mechanism for preventing too low a level of blood sugar. Abramowitz, Hisaw and Papandrea (1944) showed that injection of eyestalk extracts into the crab *Callinectes* led to a raised blood sugar level still obvious after five hours. One hour after injection of 0·001 eyestalk equivalent, the blood sugar level was twice the normal value. These workers found that the greater part of the activity resided in the sinus gland. Neither they, nor later Kleinholz and his collaborators (Kleinholz and Little, 1948, 1949; Kleinholz, Havel and Reichart, 1950), found that eyestalk removal or sinus gland removal led to a lowered blood sugar level in Brachyura or Astacura; though in the palinuran *Panulirus*, Scheer and Scheer (1951) did find such an effect of eyestalk removal. They found too (as did Kleinholz and his collaborators) that injection of eyestalk extracts into animals which lacked eyestalks or sinus glands provoked a raised blood sugar level.

Stress of any kind, as in vertebrates, leads to hyperglycaemia, and this action is certainly mediated through the eyestalks, for in animals deprived of the eyestalks stress no longer has this effect, nor does it in animals in which the X organ-sinus gland tract is cut.

To summarize these rather confusing observations: the sinus gland appears to release a diabetogenic principle which helps in maintaining the blood sugar level above a minimum. In crabs other centres outside the eyestalk may also produce this principle. It is released in response to stress and its release is stimulated *via* the X organ-sinus gland tract. Some of the blood sugar is used as a precursor for chitin in laying down the exoskeleton, so that sugar metabolism is closely connected with moulting and the endocrine control of the two may be related.

A number of experimental observations on the metabolism of chitin and glycogen have appeared in the literature and there is some suggestion of their endocrine control. The evidence, however, is so slender that it will not be discussed further.

LIPOIDS AND CAROTENOIDS. The fat reserves of crabs vary, as might be expected, with the stage of the moult cycle (Renaud, 1949; Travis, 1955), and so does the amount of fatty acid in the blood (Damboviceanu, 1932). There is a maximum preceding the moult and a gradual decline afterwards, during metecdysis. A crab is incapable of feeding for a short time before the moult and for quite a time afterwards. Renaud is of the opinion that the fatty substances in the body are of importance for the imbibition of water during ecdysis and Travis has suggested that they are used in the formation of new integument and are important in the transport of calcium. Certainly their metabolism is closely associated with the vicissitudes of the moult cycle, but there is no evidence that they are under endocrine control.

The fat-soluble carotenoids of the body, which are often stored in large amounts in the blood and hepatopancreas, seem to be under hormonal control. Changes of colour due to deposition and mobilization of carotenoids in the integument occur in many species in addition to the colour changes produced by migration of pigments within the chromatophores. In *Uca* there are noticeable changes in pigmentation shortly before the moult. Guyselman (1953) has shown that these do not take place after eyestalk removal. Conversely in *Carcinus* eyestalk removal leads to the formation of much cobalt blue pigmentation while the crabs become otherwise much paler than usual after two or three moults. These changes occur if the vision of the crab is not impaired but the sinus gland alone is removed. When the sinus gland eventually regenerates, normal pigmentation is resumed. We may presume that one of the hormones of the X organ-sinus gland complex influences the deposition of carotenoids in the integument.

PROTEINS AND NITROGEN. Despite a certain confusion of contradictory or apparently contradictory results, it seems probable that some aspects of the metabolism of nitrogen and proteins are under hormonal control. Indeed, this follows almost inevitably from the hormonal control of growth. It seems that the X organ-sinus gland complex produces some factor which restrains catabolism and perhaps shifts metabolism towards increased anabolism (Needham, 1955; Neiland and Scheer, 1953). Conditions of feeding or starvation make such differences in this type of experiment that it is often difficult to extrapolate from one man's results to another's, and this may account for much of the confusion which exists in this field.

CALCIUM. Before moulting, crustaceans with a calcified exoskeleton withdraw calcium from the shell and store it in a variety of organs, such as the hepatopancreas, gastroliths (deposits of calcium salts in the walls of the stomach), the sterna of the thoracic segments (Isopoda), or simply in the blood stream, which may become so filled with calcium salts that a wounded crab appears to bleed milk. After the shell is cast the initial hardening of the new shell seems to be effected by redeposition of this calcium, to which is added more absorbed from the surrounding water through the gills or over the general body surface. There is much evidence to suggest that this calcium cycle, which is so closely related to the moulting cycle, is under the control of endocrine substances of the eyestalks and that the two cycles are under one control.

There is often less calcium in the cast shell after eyestalk removal than in a shell cast by an intact individual (Guyselman, 1953). But more direct evidence on endocrine control of the calcium metabolism by the eyestalks comes from the work of Kyer (1942) and Scudamore (1947) who independently found that eyestalk ablation in the winter in the crayfish *Cambarus* led to the initiation of the premoult and to the formation of gastroliths. Injection of extracts of the central nervous system reinforced the effects of eyestalk removal, thus suggesting the existence of a hormone there antagonistic to the hormone of the

89

eyestalk. Scudamore also found a diurnal rhythm in the formation of the gastroliths.

Similar observations on the calcium stores of other species have been made and substantially confirm the control by the eyestalk of these stores. Recently we have used the blood calcium level as an indication of the early stages of proecdysis (Carlisle, 1957). The overall picture that emerges is of an eyestalk hormone—possibly the moult-inhibiting hormone—that inhibits the removal of calcium from the integument and prevents stores of it being built up. It is active during anecdysis, but not during diecdysis (like the moult-inhibiting hormone), and it seems to exert its effects via the Y organ (Carlisle, 1957). At no point does it differ, so far as our knowledge goes, from the moult-inhibiting hormone, and it seems most probable that the action by the eyestalks on calcium metabolism is by means of the moult-inhibiting hormone.

PHOSPHATE. Most of the calcium in Crustacea appears to be in the form of calcium phosphate and the phosphate content of the blood and tissues changes cyclically in the same way as the calcium content (Travis, 1955). Needham (1954) and Travis have shown the importance of alkaline phosphatase in this cycle. In most ways calcium and phosphate seem to go together, and one is tempted to assume that there is unified control. But Travis (1952 b) has shown that eyestalk removal may lead to an alteration in the blood phosphorus content while leaving the calcium content unaltered in *Panulirus*. She showed that the factor responsible for this did not reside in the sinus gland and suggested the X organs as the site. It is thus apparent that whatever principle has this effect on the phosphorus of the blood, the metabolism of this element is not under identical control with the calcium.

It is possible that the phosphorus which responds in this way to eyestalk removal is not the inorganic phosphate, which may still be under the same control as the calcium, but some form of organic phosphorus, for it is known that the tissues of Crustacea are especially rich in high-energy organic phosphates.

By the use of radioactive phosphorus the rate of turnover has been estimated and shown to be remarkably high. This suggests that there is a dynamic equilibrium of stored phosphorus, with, presumably, control mechanism for regulating both anabolic and catabolic changes.

There is a regular cycle, associated with the moult cycle, of rate of oxygen consumption and respiratory quotient. In proecdysis oxygen consumption increases and R.Q. drops (Bliss, 1953) (cf. fig. 16). Eyestalk removal has been shown, in many species, to produce a respiration characteristic of proecdysis. This is not a result of sinus gland extirpation, for after this operation both rate of consumption of oxygen and R.Q. remain much the same in the land crab *Gecarcinus*. The crab, however, loses the ability to vary either in response to the demands of the moment. Bliss interprets these results as implying that a hormone controlling oxygen consumption and R.Q. is formed in some tissue in the eyestalk and released at the sinus gland. The sinus gland presumably then controls the rate of release. When the sinus glands are removed the production and release of the hormone continues, but at an unregulated rate.

Rate of oxygen consumption and R.Q. are only symptoms of catabolic processes and it seems likely that it is hormonal control of some catabolic process that we are investigating when considering these phenomena. Perhaps the data which have been obtained on proteins and nitrogen metabolism fit here. At the cellular or sub-cellular level the effect of eyestalk extracts is still to be seen, for Scheer, Schwabe and Scheer (1952) have demonstrated the effects of these extracts on the metabolic rate of muscle homogenates.

DEVELOPMENT

In the adult most of the moults which occur are more or less the same and the foregoing account of the hormonal control of moulting and of the associated phenomena might apply to any of them. But certain of the moults have special characteristics. The prepuberal moult, at which the sex of the juvenile first becomes apparent though the animal is not yet mature, is one example about whose endocrinology we have as yet no information. Nor have we any knowledge of the endocrinology of the moults of metamorphosis. About other special moults we are, however, beginning to learn something.

. THE FINAL MOULT. In some species of decapods (we have no information about other groups) the cycle of growth and moulting terminates with a final moult after which the animal never moults again. This, among other results, lays an upper limit to the size which a species may attain. Teissier (1935) was, so far as we are aware, the first to draw attention to this phenomenon. The term intermoult, for the stage after the last moult, becomes completely unusable, since the anecdysis which follows this moult is in no sense between two moults. This stage in the life history of the animal can be called the terminal anecdysis. Species in which the occurrence of the final moult is established include the spider crab *Maia*, *Carcinus*, *Callinectes* and *Pachygrapsus*. The last is the best documented species (Hiatt, 1948). It may be inferred in *Portunus*, and in fact in any species where there is a definite upper size limit. It is unknown in *Homarus* and *Cancer pagurus* which may go on moulting and increasing in size indefinitely until overtaken by death; reports of 'giant' crabs and lobsters are not infrequent in the lay press and fishing periodicals. The largest *Homarus* we have seen recorded from British waters (the Solent) during the last ten years weighed 20 kg. and had an overall length of 120 cm.

The only investigations into the endocrinology of the final moult and terminal anecdysis are those of Carlisle (1957). Two species were investigated and the regulation of terminal anecdysis proved to be different in the two. They were the oxyrhynchan crab *Maia* and the brachyrhynchan crab *Carcinus*. In *Maia* the last moult is the moult of puberty, while in *Carcinus* the last moult is (in the Plymouth population) about the tenth or eleventh after puberty.

In *Maia* the cause of the cessation of moulting is to be found in the degeneration, after the last moult, of the Y organ. It is known that this organ is necessary for continuing moulting and its degeneration is sufficient immediate cause for a complete cessation, but nothing is known of the cause of the degeneration itself. In *Carcinus*, by contrast, the Y organ does not degenerate after the final moult and the cause of cessation of moulting is to be found in the activity of the X organ-sinus gland complex, which produces excessive amounts of the moult-inhibiting hormone after the last moult. Removal of this complex allows ecdysis to continue, so that giant crabs can be produced in the laboratory by this means, and at the same time the life span can be increased. The operation naturally has no such effect on *Maia*. In both species injection of Y organ extracts produces transiently the first sign of approaching moult, in the form of heightened blood calcium level. In *Carcinus* repeated injections led to eventual moulting. If the Y organ of *Carcinus* is removed during the terminal anecdysis, removal of the X organ-sinus gland complex no longer stimulates moulting.

In both species the cause of the cessation of moulting lies with the Y organ, but while in *Maia* this organ degenerates after the last moult and so can no longer produce the hormone necessary for moulting, in *Carcinus* it is restrained by the eyestalk complex from producing this hormone.

THE COPULATORY MOULT. Copulation can only take place in Malocostraca, with perhaps a few exceptions, when the female has just moulted and the male integument is hard. In *Maia* it can only take place between a female which has just completed the final moult and a male which last moulted the year before. In species which may breed several times after the moult of puberty, copulation similarly occurs several times, each time at a moult of the female. At this moult the female assumes the brooding characters—for example, the ovigerous hairs, oostegites—the organs for holding the fertilized eggs. At the next moult, after the eggs have hatched, she loses them again. For some time before the moult of copulation the female is exuding some substance which is attractive to the males, and in many species the female is carried about by the male during this proecdysis until she moults and copulation can take place. In many crabs the attractive substance can be detected by the males at a distance, but in *Leander* it is only effective if the male touches the female.

It seems likely that the special features of this moult are under endocrine control, and it is known that the appearance of the brooding characters is so controlled (see next chapter); but nothing is known about the control of the behaviour and the production of the attractive substance (pherormone) by the female.

THE CRITICAL MOULTS OF SEX REVERSAL. Some species of Natantia, chiefly among the Pandaloidea, are protandric hermaphrodites. After a period as males they reverse sex to become female. In *Lysmata* every individual is a protandric hermaphrodite, but in some species there may be a small percentage of individuals which are primary females, starting life as that sex. In *Pandalus borealis* about 5 % are primary females, in *P. montagui* about 35 %, and in *P. bonniori* there is no sex reversal at all.

Throughout the greater part of the male phase a developing ovary is present, and the testis may persist after sex reversal. At any one moment it is not the state of the gonad which determines the functional sex of the protandric hermaphrodite, but the nature of the secondary and accessory sexual characters. An animal which possesses a vas deferens and the male copulatory appendages can copulate as a male, but not as a female, while one in which the vas deferens is closed cannot function as a male even if the testis is still producing sperm.

At the first critical moult the protandric hermaphrodite loses the copulatory appendages, and the new shell is complete over the male genital pore so that the vas deferens no longer opens to the exterior. The animal can no longer function as a male. This moult may thus leave the animal as a sterile intersex in which neither the male nor the female ducts open to the exterior, but in favourable conditions of season and nutrition the same moult may see the appearance of the female characters —the opening of the oviduct on the third thoracic segment and the development of the brooding characters. In such a case the animal can immediately copulate as a female; so that the same individual has been seen to copulate as a male 90 minutes before moulting and as a female 10 minutes after. In less favourable circumstances the development of the female characters is delayed for one to three moults and they first appear at a moult of copulation—that is to say, the brooding characters appear at the same moult as the opening of the oviduct so that the animal is immediately able to mate as a female.

In some respects the critical moults of sex reversal seem to be under hormonal control, for eyestalk removal in *Lysmata* increases the proportion which reverse sex at the next moult. Injection of eyestalk extracts prevents this and in intact animals reduces the proportion which reverse sex. The same situation is seen in *Pandalus borealis* (Carlisle, 1953 c, 1956 a, b). The principle concerned appears to reside in the sinus gland and M.T.G.X. There is some evidence that it may be the ovary-inhibiting hormone which is concerned in the regulation of sex reversal.

CHAPTER 6

Sex

THOUGH some species of Natantia, as discussed in the last chapter, show protandric hermaphroditism, most of the Malacostraca are bisexual animals in which the sex is determined genetically. But the structural and functional expression of the genetic sex is to a large extent hormonally controlled. In the juvenile the gonads cannot come to maturity without the action of the Y organ; in the adult the androgenic or vas deferens gland is needed for the development of the testis, and this gland is able to convert by its hormonal action ovary into testis. The breeding cycles are controlled by eyestalk hormones and the brooding characters develop under the influence of secretions of the ovary.

In the juvenile crab, after metamorphosis but before puberty, ablation of the Y organ leads to a considerable retardation of gametogenesis and to degenerative changes in the gonads in either sex (Echalier, 1954; Arvy, Echalier and Gabe, 1954). If the operation is performed after sexual maturity, however, no effect is observed on the gonads, which continue to function normally. Two hypotheses have been advanced to explain these observations: (1) that the gonadal anomalies in the immature animals deprived of the Y organ are only a particular aspect of a very general disturbance of the metabolism of the animals; (2) that the Y organ elaborates a specific hormonal principle whose action is needed for the maturation of the gonad, but which is not necessary for the continued functioning of the gonad, once this is fully ripe. No results presented so far permit one to decide between these two hypotheses. It may be noted that the action of the Y organ upon the gonads is not sexually specific, and injection of extracts or implantation of fragments from either sex will cause continued development of the gonads.

Far different is the action of the androgenic gland or vas deferens gland described by Charniaux-Cotton. This gland has now been observed in all orders of the Malacostraca except the

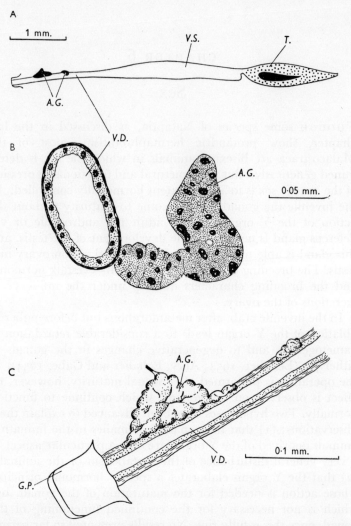

Fig. 18. The androgenous gland or vas deferens gland of *Orchestia gammarella*. A, the testis, with the vas deferens opening at the genital papilla, showing the position of the gland on the distal part of the vas deferens; notice the accessory glandular tissue lying proximal to the main gland. B. Transverse section of the vas deferens and gland. C. Dissection of the distal portion of the vas deferens and gland, showing the macroscopic appearance. *A.G.,* androgenous gland; *G.P.,* genital papilla; *T.,* testis; *V.D.,* vas deferens; *V.S.,* vesicula seminalis. (Redrawn from Charniaux-Cotton, 1956*b*.)

Isopoda. It lies near the distal end of the vas deferens attached to its wall. In the amphipod *Orchestia*, in which it was first described, it takes the form of a pyramidal mass of cells, about 250μ across the base, which lies against the vas deferens. Smaller masses of similar structure are frequently found a little proximally along the vas deferens. The cells are more or less equal, isodiametric, and show histological evidence of secretion. There is no obvious vascularization and no secretory duct. In *Carcinus* it is present attached to the subterminal portion of the vas deferens. Here it is a vermiform structure about 7 mm. long and may entwine the vas deferens. Its diameter is only 35μ despite its length. It is divided longitudinally into two parts which twist round each other. In transverse section may be seen more or less circular masses of cells about $6-7\mu$ in diameter, with clearly marked cell walls. The cytoplasm is vacuolated (Charniaux-Cotton, 1956*a*).

Charniaux-Cotton has performed all the published work on this organ so far and a good summary of this is to be found in her paper (1956*b*). She has shown that this organ is necessary for the development of a testis. If an ovary is implanted into a male *Orchestia*, even if the animal has been castrated, the ovary is converted into a testis and may go on to produce sperm. If the androgenic gland is transplanted into a female, all the primary, secondary and accessory characters become male— the ovary is converted into a testis and copulatory organs develop, together with all the other modifications of anatomy and behaviour found in the male. The converted females will even carry about a female and go through the whole courtship ceremony, but are not capable of fertilizing a female. If the androgenic gland is removed from a male, whether or not it is at the same time castrated, the male characters regress and at succeeding moults are replaced by female organs. An ovary transplanted into such a male, even if the animal's own testis is still present, will survive unmodified.

In the isopods, where the androgenic gland has not been observed, the testis exerts an exactly similar influence to this gland, even to the extent of converting implanted ovary into testis, or, when implanted into a female, converting her ovary into testis (Lattin & Gross, 1953; Legrand, 1954).

In the male the breeding cycle in most species is not very obvious. Males may be ripe throughout the year. Nevertheless, Démeusy (1953) has found that removal of eyestalks from immature or non-breeding male crabs leads to a great increase in the size of the testis and of the vas deferens. She interprets this as evidence that the eyestalk secretes a hormone responsible for inhibiting the development of the testis outside the breeding season. She has published no experiments which might show the site of origin of this postulated hormone within the eyestalk. In the natantian *Lysmata* I have found that eyestalk removal has no effect whatsoever on the weight of the testes or degree of development of the vasa deferentia, nor has injection of eyestalk extracts (Carlisle, 1954c). On the contrary, removal of the eyestalk of functional males of this protandrous hermaphrodite results in an increase in size of the ovarian portion of the gonad, leaving the testicular portion unaffected. This is not unexpected, since hormonal control frequently differs widely between the Natantia and the Reptantia.

The breeding cycle in the female is far more pronounced. Some species of course, such as *Maia*, breed only once and there is no breeding cycle, but in most species breeding follows a definite pattern. Many observers, starting with Panouse (1943), have found that eyestalk removal, in most groups of decapods, leads to a rapid increase in the size of the ovary and to premature oviposition, if the operation is performed in immature females, or in females at a time when the animals are not breeding. Removal of the sinus gland alone leads to some increase in ovarian size, but not nearly so great an increase as after eyestalk ablation (Panouse, 1944, 1946). This growth of the ovary can be partially or wholly prevented by implanting sinus gland tissue into the abdomina of operated animals, and the normal growth of the ovary which precedes the breeding season can likewise be prevented by injection of extracts of whole eyestalks, of sinus gland, or of the $M.T.G.X.$ (Carlisle, 1953c). I have found that the principle responsible for the inhibition of ovarian growth is to be found in the sinus gland and in the $M.T.G.X.$, but is absent from the rest of the eyestalk. It seems probable that, like the other hormones found in the sinus gland, the ovary-inhibiting hormone is produced in the neurosecretory cells of the *M.T.G.X.* and passed down the axons to the sinus gland.

To speak correctly, the ovary-inhibiting hormone is responsible for restraining vitellogenesis outside the breeding season. As the breeding season approaches the titre of ovary-inhibiting hormone in the eyestalks drops steadily and vitellogenesis begins. It is this which is responsible for the great increase in size of the ovary. The hormone appears to exert a direct action on the ovary, and has been shown to be active in the absence of the Y organ. Once the yolk has begun to appear, the ovary begins to produce a principle which is responsible for the development of the brooding characters. These do not appear till the next moult, but their production begins during proecdysis. They include in different species ovigerous hairs, brood pouches and other characters. This action of the ripening ovary has been demonstrated by means of castration of the female, by irradiation or surgical methods, followed in some experiments by the implantation of ovarian tissue. Castration prevents the appearance of the cyclical brooding characters, except after the implantation of ripening ovary (Knowles and Callan, 1940; Takewaki and Nakamura, 1944; Charniaux, 1952, 1953a, b; Charniaux-Cotton, 1954a, b; among others). Balesdent-Marquet (1953) has concluded that even the brooding characters are not fully regulated by the ovary, but may be influenced by some other hormonal factor.

The protandric hermaphrodites show a cycle of production of the ovary-inhibiting hormone which may have some bearing on the sex reversal. The amount present in the eyestalks is high throughout the male phase, thus inhibiting the ovarian portion of the gonad. Towards the end of the male phase the amount drops to a low level and vitellogenesis begins. At the next moult the animal loses its external male character and may then become a temporarily sterile intersex, or may at once become a female. Since the moult at which it becomes a female is also always a moult at which it assumes the brooding characters, these latter can only appear if vitellogenesis is sufficiently far advanced to have caused their development. Removal of the eyestalks shortly before the sex reversal becomes due hastens vitellogenesis and at the same time increases the proportion of animals which become full females at the next moult (Carlisle, 1953c, 1957). Injection of eyestalk extracts has the reverse

99 7-2

effect. Clearly the appearance of the brooding characters is a result of the production of the appropriate hormone by the ripening ovary, but it seems probable that the alteration of the other external characters is an expression of direct action of eyestalk hormones on the external sexual characters. Such an action is known otherwise from the work of Cornubert, Démeusy and Veillet (1952), who found that after eyestalk ablation immature crabs assumed the adult habit prematurely. Stephens (1952), moreover, has found that the development of the cement gland of the oviduct of the female crayfish is accelerated by eyestalk ablation, a further effect of the eyestalk hormones on the secondary sexual characters.

The circum-orbital gland has been described in the eyestalk (not around the orbit) with a seasonal cycle of histologically demonstrated secretion. Histological evidence suggests that this secretion reaches a peak during the development of the ovary towards full reproductive activity and declines after the breeding season. Aoto and Nishida (1956), who have described this gland and its cycles, suggest that it may be antagonistic to the ovary-inhibiting hormone and thus, presumably, responsible for stimulating ovarian development. In the same paper these authors conclude that the sex reversal of *Pandalus kessleri* is not affected by eyestalk hormones and that the growth of the oocytes, which occurs at the time of sex reversal, is a result of either the release of mechanical pressure from the last discharge of sperm or of release from a 'sexual hormone from the surrounding testicular tissue which is almost completely diminished in animals changing sex'. It must, however, be pointed out that the growth of oocytes in other species of *Pandalus* and in *Lysmata* long precedes the last release of sperm and that sperm production may go on even after sex reversal; while no one has ever been able to find any evidence for a testicular hormone inhibiting the ovary in any way. Indeed, Charniaux-Cotton (1954a) found that testicular implants into female *Ochestia* did not interfere in the slightest with the ovary and the hosts oviposited normally.

The simplest conclusion compatible with current knowledge is that the breeding cycle of the female is controlled by the ovary-inhibiting hormone of the eyestalk and that the ripening ovary is responsible for the production of the hormone which stimulates the appearance of the brooding characters.

In the protandric hermaphrodites the testis may degenerate either before or after sex-reversal. This seems to be the result of the degeneration of the vas deferens gland which takes place at about this time and can be provoked by cautery of the gland in *Pandalus* (Carlisle, unpublished).

Of the hormones concerned in the regulation of sexual matters in Decapoda, only the ovary-inhibiting hormone of the eye-stalk has been investigated chemically. This hormone appears to be similar to the substance produced by queen bees which inhibits the ovaries of the worker bees. Both substances seem to be steroids (Carlisle and Butler, 1956). To speak more particularly, an apparently steroidal substance with ovary-inhibiting properties may be obtained from the sinus gland by extraction methods which involve denaturation of proteins. This substance is no longer water-soluble. The naturally occurring hormone appears to be a conjugate steroid-protein complex, which is, of course, freely soluble in water. Denaturation of the protein releases the insoluble steroid, which, however, retains all the biological properties of the hormone.

CHAPTER 7

Conclusion: The Fourth Phase

IN the introduction we have suggested that crustacean endocrinology has passed through three phases since its inception in 1928. During the first ten years the presence of chromactivating hormones was demonstrated and the sinus gland suggested as the source of these substances. During the second phase (1939–50) the multiplicity of hormones concerned in pigment movements was demonstrated and other sources of hormones within the nervous system suspected; during this second phase the influence of hormones on many other functions of the body besides pigments became apparent. The third phase, which seems to be approaching its end now, began in 1951 when it was shown that most of the known endocrine systems in crustaceans were neurosecretory in nature and that the hormones were produced by modified neurones and transported along inside the axons to the blood stream. In the last six years we have seen the major endocrine systems of crustaceans clarified in the details of their structure and the main outlines of biological endocrinology mapped out in the higher Malacostraca. Enormous gaps remain on this map, but the principle outlines are there.

What is the fourth phase of crustacean endocrinology to be like? At present two main lines of progress are being actively followed, lines quite different from those that have produced the major advances in the past. These are the study of the structure of the endocrine organs by means of the electron microscope, and the biochemical investigation of the hormones. It seems to us that the fourth phase of crustacean endocrinology will be dominated by these lines of approach, though much work remains to be done, and will be done, of the kinds which have proved so fruitful in earlier phases, particularly on the hormonal control of metabolic processes. It would be pleasant to believe that the near future might see investigations into the endocrinology of other groups of Crustacea than the Malacostraca, but this seems a remote possibility. Indeed, it is only within the last few years that much attention has been paid to any order but the Decapoda. Much in the biology of copepods, for example, is suggestive of endocrine control, but the possibility has been investigated neither physiologically, nor by the technically easier (considering the size of the animals) methods of histology; we do not even know if the Entomostraca, or any one order of the Entomostraca, possess any of the endocrine organs apparent in the Malacostraca. Here is a field of research which is wide open to any newcomer.

Finally, is it too much to hope that by combining our increasing knowledge of crustacean hormones with the data of insect and vertebrate endocrinology we may perhaps eventually obtain some insight into the basic nature of hormones and their evolution?

REFERENCES

ABRAMOWITZ, A. A. (1936a). Action of crustacean eyestalk extract on melanophores of hypophysectomized fish, amphibians and reptiles. *Proc. Soc. exp. Biol., N.Y.*, **34**, 714– .

ABRAMOWITZ, A. A. (1936b). The action of intermedin on crustacean melanophores and of the crustacean hormone on elasmobranch melanophores. *Proc. nat. Acad. Sci., Wash.*, **22**, 521–3.

ABRAMOWITZ, A. A. (1937a). The chromatophorotropic hormone of the Crustacea: standardization, properties and physiology of the eyestalk glands. *Biol. Bull., Woods Hole*, **72**, 344–65.

ABRAMOWITZ, A. A. (1937b). The comparative physiology of pigmentary responses in the Crustacea. *J. exp. Zool.* **76**, 407–22.

ABRAMOWITZ, A. A. (1938). The similarity between the hypophyseal chromatophorotropic hormone and the chromatophorotropic hormone of the crustacean eyestalk. *Physiol. Zöol.* **11**, 299–311.

ABRAMOWITZ, A. A. (1940). Purification of the chromatophorotropic hormone of the crustacean eyestalk. *J. biol. Chem.* **132**, 501–6.

ABRAMOWITZ, R. K. and ABRAMOWITZ, A. A. (1939). Moulting and viability after removal of the eyestalk in *Uca pugilator*. *Biol. Bull., Woods Hole*, **77**, 326–7.

ABRAMOWITZ, R. K. and ABRAMOWITZ, A. A. (1940). Moulting, growth and survival after eyestalk removal in *Uca pugilator*. *Biol. Bull., Woods Hole*, **78**, 179–88.

ABRAMOWITZ, A. A., HISAW, F. L. and PAPANDREA, D. N. (1944). The occurrence of a diabetogenic factor in the eyestalks of crustaceans. *Biol. Bull., Woods Hole*, **86**, 1–5.

ALEXANDROWICZ, J. S. (1952). Notes on the nervous system in the Stomatopoda. I. The system of median connectives. *Pubbl. Staz. zool. Napoli*, **23**, 201–14.

ALEXANDROWICZ, J. S. (1953a). Nervous organs in the pericardial cavity of the decapod Crustacea. *J. mar. biol. Ass. U.K.* **31**, 563–80.

ALEXANDROWICZ, J. S. (1953b). Notes on the nervous system in the Stomatopoda. II. The system of dorsal trunks. *Pubbl. Staz. zool. Napoli*, **24**, 29–39.

ALEXANDROWICZ, J. S. (1953c). Notes on the nervous system in the Stomatopoda. III. Small nerve cells in motor nerves. *Pubbl. Staz. zool. Napoli*, **24**, 39–45.

ALEXANDROWICZ, J. S. (1954). Innervation of an amphipod heart. *J. mar. biol. Ass. U.K.* **33**, 709–19.

ALEXANDROWICZ, J. S. (1955). Innervation of the heart of *Praunus flexuosus* (Mysidacea). *J. mar. biol. Ass. U.K.* **34**, 47–53.

ALEXANDROWICZ, J. S. and CARLISLE, D. B. (1953). Some experiments on the function of the pericardial organs in Crustacea. *J. mar. biol. Ass. U.K.* **32**, 175–92.

AMAR, R. (1948). Un organ endocrine chez *Idotea*. *C.R. Acad. Sci., Paris*, **227**, 301–3.

AMAR, R. (1950). Les formations endocrines cérébrales des Isopodes marins. *C.R. Acad. Sci., Paris*, **230**, 407–9.

AMAR, R. (1951). Formations endocrines cérébrales des Isopodes marins et comportement chromatique d'*Idotea*. Thesis, Paris, 139 pp.

AMAR, R. (1953). Sur l'existence de cellules neurosécrétrices dans le cerveau de *Rocinela* (Crustacea Isopoda). *Bull. Soc. zool. Fr.* **78**, 171–3.

AOTO, T. and NISHIDA, H. (1956). Effect of removal of the eyestalks on the growth and maturation of the oocytes in a hermaphrodite prawn, *Pandalus kessleri*. *J. Fac. Sci. Hokkaido Univ.* (Ser. 6, Zool.), **12**, 412–24.

ARVY, L., ECHALIER, G. and GABE, M. (1954). Modifications de la gonade de *Carcinides (Carcinus) moenas* L. (Crustacé décapode), après ablation bilaterale de l'organe Y. *C.R. Acad. Sci., Paris*, **239**, 1853–5.

BALESDENT-MARQUET, M. L. (1953). Remarques sur le cycle ovarien, le cycle des mues et les caractères sexuels secondaires chez le Crustacé isopode *Asellus aquaticus* Linné. *C.R. Acad. Sci., Paris*, **236**, 1086–8.

BECKER, E. (1941). Die Pigmente der Ommin- und Ommatingruppe, eine neue Klasse von Naturfarbstoffen. *Naturwissenschaften*, **29**, 237.

BELLONCI, G. (1882). Sistema nervoso e organi dei sensi della *Sphaeroma serratum*. *Atti Accad. Roma* (3), **10**, 91.

BLASCHKO, H., HAGEN, P. and WELCH, A. D. (1953). Observations on the intracellular granules of the adrenal medulla. *J. Physiol.* **129**, 27–49.

BLISS, D. E. (1951). Metabolic effect of sinus gland or eyestalk removal in the land crab, *Gecarcinus lateralis*. *Anat. Rec.* **111**, p. 502.

BLISS, D. E. (1953). Endocrine control of metabolism in the land crab *Gecarcinus lateralis* (Fréminville). I. Differences in the respiratory metabolism of sinusglandless and eyestalkless crabs. *Biol. Bull., Woods Hole*, **104**, pp. 275–96.

BLISS, D. E. (1956). Neurosecretion and the control of growth in a decapod crustacean. *Bertil Hanstron. Zoological papers in honour of his 65th birthday*. (Ed. Wingstrand, K. G.)

BLISS, D. E., DURAND, J. B. and WELSH, J. H. (1954). Neurosecretory systems in decapod Crustacea. *Z. Zellforsch.* **39**, 520–36.

BLISS, D. E. and WELSH, J. H. (1952). The neurosecretory system of brachyuran Crustacea. *Biol. Bull., Woods Hole*, **103**, 157–69.

BOWMAN, T. E. (1949). Chromatophorotropins in the central nervous organs of the crab, *Hemigrapsus oregonensis*. *Biol. Bull., Woods Hole*, **96**, 238–45.

BROWN, F. A. (1933). The controlling mechanism of chromatophores in *Palaemonetes*. *Proc. nat. Acad. Sci., Wash.*, **19**, 327–9.

BROWN, F. A. (1934). The chemical nature of the pigments and the transformations responsible for colour changes in *Palaemonetes*. *Biol. Bull., Woods Hole*, **47**, 365.

BROWN, F. A. (1935 a). Colour changes in *Palaemonetes*. *J. Morph.* **57**, 317–34.

BROWN, F. A. (1935 b). Control of pigment migration within the chromatophores of *Palaemonetes vulgaris*. *J. exp. Zool.* **71**, 1–14.

BROWN, F. A. (1940). The crustacean sinus-gland and chromatophore activation. *Physiol. Zöol.* **13**, 343–55.

BROWN, F. A. (1942). Sinus gland extirpation in the crayfish without eye-stalk removal. *Proc. Soc. exp. Biol.*, *N.Y.*, **50**, 295–7.

BROWN, F. A. (1944). Hormones in the Crustacea. Their sources and activities. *Quart. Rev. Biol.*, **19**, 118–43.

BROWN, F. A. (1946). The source and activity of *Crago*-darkening hormone. *Physiol. Zöol.* **19**, 215–23.

BROWN, F. A. (1946). Endocrine activity of the tritocerebral commissure of *Crago* (Crustacea). *Anat. Rec.* **94**, 405.

BROWN, F. A. (1948a). Colour changes in the stomatopod crustacean *Chloridella empusa*. *Anat. Rec.* **101**, 732–3.

BROWN, F. A. (1948b). Hormones in Crustaceans. *The Hormones*. (G. Pincus and K. Thimann edit.). Acad. Press, New York, pp. 159–200.

BROWN, F. A. (1949). The mechanism of colour changes in Crustaceans. *The Collecting Net*, **19**, No. 1, 8–12.

BROWN, F. A. (1950). Studies on the physiology of *Uca* red chromatophores. *Biol. Bull.*, *Woods Hole*, **98**, 218–26.

BROWN, F. A. (1952). Hormones in crustaceans. In *The Actions of Hormones in Plants and Invertebrates*, New York.

BROWN, F. A. and CUNNINGHAM, O. (1939). Influence of the sinus gland of crustaceans on normal viability and ecdysis. *Biol. Bull.*, *Woods Hole*, **77**, 104.

BROWN, F. A. and CUNNINGHAM, U. (1941). Upon the presence and distribution of a chromatophorotropic principle in the central nervous system of *Limulus*. *Biol. Bull.*, *Woods Hole*, **81**, 80–95.

BROWN, F. A. and EDERSTROM, H. E. (1940). Dual control of certain black chromatophores of *Crago*. *J. exp. Zool.* **85**, 53–69.

BROWN, F. A., EDERSTROM, H. E. and SCUDAMORE, H. H. (1939). Sinus-gland-ectomy in crustaceans without blinding. *Anat. Rec.* **75**, suppl. 129–30.

BROWN, F. A. and FINGERMAN, M. (1951). Differentiation of black and red-dispersing factors from the brain of the fiddler crab, *Uca*. *Fed. Proc.* **10**, 20–1.

BROWN, F. A., GUYSELMAN, J. B. and SANDEEN, M. (1949). Black chromatophores of *Uca* as independent effectors. *Anat. Rec.* **105**, 615.

BROWN, F. A., HINES, M. N. and FINGERMAN, M. (1952). Hormonal regulation of the distal retinal pigment of *Palaemonetes*. *Biol. Bull.*, *Woods Hole*, **102**, 212–25.

BROWN, F. A. and JONES, G. M. (1947). Hormonal inhibition of ovarian growth in the crayfish, *Cambarus*. *Anat. Rec.* **99**, 657.

BROWN, F. A. and JONES, G. M. (1949). Ovarian inhibition by a sinus-gland principle in the fiddler crab. *Biol. Bull.*, *Woods Hole*, **91**, 228–32.

BROWN, F. A. and KLOTZ, I. M. (1946). Separation of two mutually antagonistic chromatophorotropins from the tritocerebral commissure of *Crago*. *Proc. Soc. exp. Biol.*, *N.Y.*, **64**, 310.

BROWN, F. A. and MEGLITSCH, A. (1940). Comparison of the chromatophorotropic activity of insect corpora cardiaca with that of crustacean sinus-glands. *Biol. Bull.*, *Woods Hole*, **79**, 409–18.

BROWN, F. A. and SAIGH, L. M. (1946). The comparative distribution of two chromatophorotropic hormones (CDH and CBLH) in crustacean nervous systems. *Anat. Rec.* **94**, 404.

BROWN, F. A. and SANDEEN, M. (1946). An influence of light intensity upon the responses to hormones of chromatophores of eyestalkless *Uca*. *Anat. Rec.* **96**, 179.

BROWN, F. A., SANDEEN, M. I. and WEBB, H. M. (1948). The influence of illumination on the chromatophore system of *Palaemonetes vulgaris*. *Anat. Rec.* **101**, 733.

BROWN, F. A. and SCUDAMORE, H. M. (1940). Differentiation of two principles from the crustacean sinus-gland. *J. cell. comp. Physiol.* **15**, 103-19.

BROWN, F. A., WEBB, H. M. and SANDEEN, M. I. (1952). The action of two hormones regulating the red chromatophores of *Palaemonetes*. *J. exp. Zool.* **120**, 391.

BROWN, F. A. and WULFF, V. J. (1941a). Different pigmentary types in *Crago* and their humoral control. *Bull. Mt. Desert Is. Biol. Lab.* 27-8.

BROWN, F. A. and WULFF, V. J. (1941b). Chromatophore types in *Crago* and their endocrine control. *J. cell. comp. Physiol.* **18**, 339-53.

BUSNEL, R. G. and DRILHON, A. (1948). Sur les pigments flaviniques et ptériniques des Crustacés. *Bull. Soc. zool. Fr.* **73**, 143.

CARLISLE, D. B. (1953a). Studies on *Lysmata seticaudata* Risso (Crustacea Decapoda). III. On the activity of the moult-accelerating principle when administered by the oral route. *Pubbl. Staz. zool. Napoli,* **24**, 279-85.

CARLISLE, D. B. (1953b). Studies on *Lysmata seticaudata* Risso (Crustacea Decapoda). IV. On the site of origin of the moult-accelerating principle—experimental evidence. *Pubbl. Staz. zool. Napoli,* **24**, 285-92.

CARLISLE, D. B. (1953c). Studies on *Lysmata seticaudata* Risso (Crustacea Decapoda). V. The ovarian inhibiting hormone and the hormonal inhibition of sex-reversal. *Pubbl. Staz. zool. Napoli,* **24**, 355-72.

CARLISLE, D. B. (1953d). Studies on *Lysmata seticaudata* Risso (Crustacea Decapoda). VI. Notes on the structure of the neurosecretory system of the eyestalk. *Pubbl. Staz. zool. Napoli,* **24**, 435-47.

CARLISLE, D. B. (1953e). Note préliminaire sur la structure du système neurosécréteur du pédoncule oculaire de *Lysmata seticaudata* Risso (Crustacea). *C.R. Acad. Sci., Paris,* **236**, 2541-2.

CARLISLE, D. B. (1953f). Moulting hormones in *Leander* (Crustacea Decapoda). *J. mar. biol. Ass. U.K.* **32**, 289-96.

CARLISLE, D. B. (1954a). On the hormonal inhibition of moulting in decapod Crustacea. *J. mar. biol. Ass. U.K.* **33**, 61-3.

CARLISLE, D. B. (1954b). Studies on *Lysmata seticaudata* Risso (Crustacea Decapoda). VII. The lack of influence of eyestalk ablation and of injection of eyestalk extracts on testicular weight and degree of development of the male genital ducts. *Pubbl. Staz. zool. Napoli,* **25**, 241-5.

CARLISLE, D. B. (1954c). The X organ-sinus gland complex, somatotropin, the ovarian inhibiting hormone and sex-reversal in *Lysmata* (Natantia, Hippolytidae). *Pubbl. Staz. zool. Napoli,* **24**, suppl. 79-80.

CARLISLE, D. B. (1955). Local variations in the colour pattern of the prawn *Leander serratus* (Pennant). *J. mar. biol. Ass. U.K.* **34**, 559-63.

CARLISLE, D. B. (1956a). On the hormonal control of water balance in *Carcinus*. *Pubbl. Staz. zool. Napoli,* **27**, 227-31.

CARLISLE, D. B. (1956b). An indole-alkylamine regulating heart-beat in Crustacea. *Biochem. J.* **63**, 32.

CARLISLE, D. B. (1957). On the hormonal inhibition of moulting in decapod Crustacea. II. The terminal anecdysis in crabs. *J. mar. biol. Ass. U.K.* **36**, 291–307.

CARLISLE, D. B. and BUTLER, C. G. (1956). The 'queen-substance' of honeybees and the ovary inhibiting hormone of crustaceans. *Nature, Lond.*, **177**, 276–7.

CARLISLE, D. B. and DOHRN, P. F. R. (1952). Sulla presenza di un ormone d'accrescimento in un crostaceo decapode, la *Lysmata seticaudata* Risso. *Ric. sci., Torino*, **23**, 95–100.

CARLISLE, D. B. and DOHRN, P. F. R. (1953). Studies on *Lysmata seticaudata* Risso (Crustacea Decapoda). II. Experimental evidence for a growth- and moult-accelerating factor obtainable from eyestalks. *Pubbl. Staz. zool. Napoli*, **24**, 69–83.

CARLISLE, D. B., DUPONT-RAABE, M. and KNOWLES, F. G. W. (1955). Recherches préliminaires relatives à la séparation et à la comparaison des substances chromactives des Crustacés et des Insectes. *C.R. Acad. Sci., Paris*, **240**, 665.

CARLISLE, D. B. and KNOWLES, F. G. W. (1953). Neurohaemal organs in Crustaceans. *Nature, Lond.*, **172**, 404–5.

CARLISLE, D. B. and PASSANO, L. M. (1953). The X-organ of Crustacea. *Nature, Lond.*, **171**, 1070–1.

CARLSON, S. P. (1935). The colour changes in *Uca pugilator*. *Proc. nat. Acad. Sci.* **21**, 549–51.

CARLSON, S. P. (1936). Colour changes in Brachyura crustaceans, especially in *Uca pugilator*. *Kungl. fysiogr. Sällsk. Lund Forhandl.* **6**, 63–80.

CARSTAM, S. P. (1942). Weitere Beiträge zur Farbwechsel-Physiologie der Crustaceen. *Z. vergl. Physiol.* **29**, 433–72.

CARSTAM, S. P. (1949). Colour change and colour hormones in crustaceans. *Bull. Biol.* (Suppl.) **33**, 139.

CARSTAM, S. P. (1951). Enzymatic inactivation of the pigment hormone of the crustacean sinus gland. *Nature, Lond.*, **167**, 321.

CARSTAM, S. P. and SUNESON, S. (1949). Pigment activation in *Idothea neglecta* and *Leander adspersus*. *Kungl. fysiogr. Sällsk. Handl.* (2), **4**, 355.

CHARNIAUX, H. (1952). Castration chirurgicale chez un Crustacé Amphipode (*Orchestia gammarella*) et déterminisme des caractères sexuels secondaires. Premiers résultats. *C.R. Acad. Sci., Paris*, **234**, 2570–2.

CHARNIAUX, H. (1953 a). Etude du déterminisme des caractères sexuels secondaires par castration chirurgicale et implantation d'ovaire chez un Crustacé Amphipode (*Orchestia gammarella*). *C.R. Acad. Sci., Paris*, **236**, 141–2.

CHARNIAUX, H. (1953 b). Existence, chez un Crustacé Amphipode, de l'action hormonale des ovaires sur un caractère sexuel secondaire. *XIV. Intern. Zool. Congr., Copenhagen.*

CHARNIAUX-COTTON, H. (1954 a). Implantation de gonades de sexe opposé à des mâles et des femelles chez un crustacé amphipode (*Orchestia gammarella*). *C.R. Acad. Sci., Paris*, **238**, 953–5.

CHARNIAUX-COTTON, H. (1954 b). Découverte chez un crustacé amphipode (*Orchestia gammarella*) d'une glande endocrine responsable de la différenciation de caractères sexuels primaires et secondaires mâles. *C.R. Acad. Sci., Paris*, **239**, 780–2.

CHARNIAUX-COTTON, H. (1956a). Existence d'un organe analogue à la 'glande androgène' chez un Pagure et un crabe. *C.R. Acad. Sci.*, *Paris*, **243**, 1168–9.

CHARNIAUX-COTTON, H. (1956b). Déterminisme hormonal de la différenciation sexuelle chez les Crustacés. *Ann. Biol.* **32**, 371–98.

CORNUBERT, G., DÉMEUSY, N. and VEILLET, A. (1952). Effets de l'ablation des pédoncules oculaires sur le développement des caractères sexuels externes des Décapodes brachyoures *Carcinus maenas* Pennant et *Pachygrapsus marmoratus* Fabricius. *C.R. Acad. Sci.*, *Paris*, **234**, 1405–7.

DAMBOVICEANU, A. (1932). Composition chimique et physico-chimique du liquide cavitaire chez les crustacés décapodes. (Physiologie de la calcification.) *Arch. Roum. Path. exp. Microbiol.* **5**, 239–309.

DEBAISIEUX, P. (1944). Les yeux des Crustacés. *La Cellule*, **50**, 9–122.

DEGNER, E. (1912a). Über Bau und Funktion der Krusterchromatophoren. *Z. wiss. Zool.* **102**, 1–78.

DEGNER, E. (1912b). Weitere Beiträge zur Kenntis der Crustaceenchromatophoren. *Z. wiss. Zool.* **102**, 701–10.

DÉMEUSY, N. (1953). Effets de l'ablation des pédoncules oculaires sur le développement de l'appareil génital mâle de *Carcinus maenas* Pennant. *C.R. Acad. Sci.*, *Paris*, **236**, 974–5.

DOHRN, R. (1905). Die Nervenendingung in Sinnesnervenzellen eines Schizopoden. *Zool. Anz.* **29**, 347.

DRACH, P. (1939). Mue et cycle d'intermue chez les Crustacés décapodes. *Ann. Inst. océanogr. Monaco*, **19**, 103–391.

DRACH, P. (1944). Étude préliminaire sur le cycle d'intermue et son conditionnement hormonal chez *Leander serratus* (Pennant). *Biol. Bull.*, *Woods Hole*, **78**, 40–62.

DURAND, J. B. (1956). Neurosecretory cell types and their secretory activity in the crayfish. *Biol. Bull.*, *Woods Hole*, **111**, 62–76.

ECHALIER, G. (1954). Recherches expérimentales sur le rôle de 'l'organe Y' dans la mue de *Carcinus moenas* (L.). Crustacé décapode. *C.R. Acad. Sci.*, *Paris*, **238**, 523–5.

ECHALIER, G. (1955). Rôle de l'organe Y dans la déterminisme de la mue de *Carcinides* (*Carcinus*) *moenas* L. (Crustacés décapodes). Expériences d'implantation. *C.R. Acad. Sci.*, *Paris*, **240**, 1581–3.

ENAMI, M. (1941a). Melanophore responses in an isopod crustacean, *Ligia exotica*. I. General responses. *Jap. J. Zool.* **9**, 497–514.

ENAMI, M. (1941b). Melanophore responses in an isopod crustacean, *Ligia exotica*. II. Humoral control of melanophores. *Jap. J. Zool.* **9**, 515.

ENAMI, M. (1943a). Chromatophore activator in the central nervous system of *Uca dubia*. *Proc. imp. Acad. Japan*, **19**, 693.

ENAMI, M. (1943b). Interspecificity of the pigmentary hormones as tested upon *Uca dubia* and upon some vertebrates. *Proc. imp. Acad. Japan*, **19**, 698.

ENAMI, M. (1950). Studies on the controlling mechanism of black chromatophores in the young of a fresh-water crab, *Sesarma haematocheir*. II. Hepato-pancreas principle antagonizing the chromatophorotropic principle from ganglionic tissues. *Seiro-Seitai*, **4**, 1.

ENAMI, M. (1951a). The sources and activities of two chromatophorotropic

hormones in crabs of the genus *Sesarma*. I. (Experimental analyses).
Biol. Bull., Woods Hole, **100**, 28–43.

ENAMI, M. (1951 *b*). The sources and activities of two chromatophorotropic
hormones in crabs of the genus *Sesarma*. II. Histology of incretory
elements. *Biol. Bull., Woods Hole*, **101**, 241–58.

FINGERMAN, M. (1956). Black pigment concentrating factor in the Fiddler
Crab. *Science*, **123**, 585–6.

FINGERMAN, F. and LOWE, M. E. (1957). Hormones controlling the chromatophores of the dwarf crawfish, *Cambarella shufeldti*: their secretion,
stability, and separation by filter-paper electrophoresis. *Tulane Studies in
Zoology*, **5**, 151–71.

FRÖHLICH, A. (1910). Farbwechselreaktion bei *Palaemon*. *Arch. EntwMech.
Org.* **29**, 432–8.

GABE, M. (1952 *a*). Particularités histochimiques de l'organe de Hanström
(organe X) et de la glande du sinus chez quelques Crustacés décapodes.
C.R. Acad. Sci., Paris, **235**, 90–2.

GABE, M. (1952 *b*). Sur l'existence d'un cycle sécrétoire dans l'organe
pseudofrontal (glande de sinus) chez *Oniscus asellus*. *C.R. Acad. Sci.,
Paris*, **235**, 900–3.

GABE, M. (1952 *c*). Particularités histologiques de la glande du sinus et de
l'organe X (organe de Bellonci) chez *Sphaeroma serratum* Fabr. *C.R.
Acad. Sci., Paris*, **235**, 973–5.

GABE, M. (1953 *a*). Quelques acquisitions récentes sur les glandes endocrines des Arthropodes. *Experientia*, **9**, 352–6.

GABE, M. (1953 *b*). Sur l'existence, chez quelques Crustacés Malacostracés,
d'un organe comparable à la glande de la mue des Insectes. *C.R. Acad.
Sci., Paris*, **237**, 1111–13.

GABE, M. (1953 *c*). Quelques applications de la coloration par la fuchsine-
paraldéhyde. *Bull. Micro. appl., Paris*, **3**, 153–62.

GABE, M. (1954). La neuro-sécrétion chez les invertébrés. *Ann. Biol.* **30**,
1–2, 1–55.

GABE, M. (1956). Histologie comparé de la glande de mue (Organe Y) des
Crustacés malacostracés. *Ann. Sci. nat. (Zool.)*, **18**, 145–52.

GEREN, B. B. (1954). The formation from the Schwann cell surface of myelin
in the peripheral nerves of chick embryos. *Exp. cell. Res.* **7**, 558–61.

GEREN, B. B. and SCHMITT, F. O. (1954). Fine structure of cells. *Rep.
Symposium, eighth Congr. cell Biol.* Noordhoff, Leiden.

GUYSELMAN, J. B. (1953). An analysis of the molting process in the fiddler
crab, *Uca pugilator*. *Biol. Bull., Woods Hole*, **104**, 115–37.

GWILLIAM, G. F. (1950). On the occurrence and solubility of a reflecting
pigment in the eyes of the Brachyura. *Anat. Rec.* **108**, 213.

HANSTRÖM, B. (1933). Neue Untersuchungen über Sinnesorgane und
Nervensystem der Crustaceen. II. *Zool. Jb., Abt. Anat. Ontog. Tiere*, **56**,
387–520.

HANSTRÖM, B. (1934 *a*). Über das Organ X, eine inkretorische Gehirndrüse
der Crustaceen. *Psychiat. neurol. Bl., Amst.*, **38**, 405–19.

HANSTRÖM, B. (1934 *b*). Neue Untersuchungen über Sinnersorgane und
Nervensystem der Crustaceen. III. *Zool. Jb., Abt. Anat. Ontog. Tiere*,
58, 101–44.

HANSTRÖM, B. (1935). Preliminary report on the probable connection between the blood gland and the chromatophore activator in decapod crustaceans. *Proc. nat. Acad. Sci., Wash.*, **21**, 584–5.

HANSTRÖM, B. (1937a). Die Sinusdrüse und der hormonal bedingte Farbwechsel der Crustaceen. *Kungl. svensk. Vetensk. Handl.* (3), **16**, No. 3, 1–99.

HANSTRÖM, B. (1937b). Inkretorische Organ und Hormonfunktionen bei den Wirbellosen. *Ergebn. Biol.* **14**, 143–224.

HANSTRÖM, B. (1939). *Hormones in Invertebrates.* Oxford.

HANSTRÖM, B. (1940). Die chromatophoraktivierende Substanz des insektenkopfes. *Lunds Univ. Arsskr. N.F. Avd.*, 2, **36**, Nr. 12; *Kungl. Fysiogr. Sällsk. Handl. N.F.*, **41**, Nr. 12.

HANSTRÖM, B. (1947a). The brain, the sense organs, and the incretory organs of the head in the Crustacea Malacostraca. *Kungl. Fysiogr. Sällsk. Handl. N.F.*, **58**, 1–44.

HANSTRÖM, B. (1947b). Three principal incretory organs in the animal kingdom. Ed. Munksgaard, Copenhagen, 67 pages.

HARA, J. (1952a). On the hormones regulating the frequency of the heart beat in the shrimp (*Paratya compressa*). *Annot. zool. Jap.* **25**, 162–71.

HARA, J. (1952b). On the effects of extracts of the grapsoid crab, *Sesarma picta*, and of the head of the pill bug, *Armadillidium vulgare*, upon the heart beat of the shrimp, *Paratya compressa*. *Annot. zool. Jap.* **25**, 411–14.

HIATT, R. W. (1948). The biology of the lined shore crab, *Pachygrapsus crassipes* Randall. *Pacif. Sci.* **2**, 135–213.

HOSOI, T. (1934). Chromatophore activating substance in the shrimps. *J. Fac. Sci. Univ. Tokyo*, **3**, 265–70.

KARLSON, P. (1956). Biochemical studies in insect hormones. *Vitamins and Hormones*, **14**, 227–266.

KEEBLE, F. and GAMBLE, F. W. (1900). The colour physiology of *Hippolyte varians*. *Proc. roy. Soc.* B, **65**, 461.

KEEBLE, F. and GAMBLE, F. W. (1903). The colour physiology of higher Crustacea. *Phil. Trans.* B, **196**, 295–388.

KEEBLE, F. and GAMBLE, F. W. (1904). The colour physiology of higher Crustacea. II. *Phil. Trans.* B, **196**, 295–388.

KEEBLE, F. W. and GAMBLE, F. (1905). The colour physiology of higher Crustacea. III. *Phil. Trans.* B, **196**, 295–388.

KLEINHOLZ, L. H. (1936). Crustacean eyestalk hormone and retinal pigment migration. *Biol. Bull., Woods Hole*, **70**, 159–84.

KLEINHOLZ, L. H. (1937a). Studies in the pigmentary system of Crustacea. I. Colour change and diurnal rhythm in *Ligia baudiniana*. *Biol. Bull., Woods Hole*, **7**, 24–36.

KLEINHOLZ, L. H. (1937b). Studies in the pigmentary system of Crustacea. II. Diurnal movements of the retinal pigments of Bermudan decapods. *Biol. Bull., Woods Hole*, **72**, 176–89.

KLEINHOLZ, L. H. (1942). Hormones in Crustacea. *Biol. Rev.* **17**, 91–119.

KLEINHOLZ, L. H. (1947). A method for removal of the sinus gland from the eyestalk of crustaceans. *Biol. Bull., Woods Hole*, **93**, 52–5.

KLEINHOLZ, L. H. (1948). Experimental hyperglycemia in the marine crustacean, *Libinia emarginata*. *Anat. Rec.* **101**, 734.

KLEINHOLZ, L. H. (1949). Response of the proximal retinal pigment of the isolated crustacean eyestalk to light and to darkness. *Proc. nat. Acad. Sci., Wash.*, **35**, 215–18.

KLEINHOLZ, L. H. (1957). Neurosecretion and retinal pigment movement in crustaceans. *Rep. 2nd internat. Symp. Neurosecretion.* Springer-Verlag, Berlin.

KLEINHOLZ, L. H. and BOURQUIN, E. (1941). Effects of eyestalk removal on decapod crustaceans. *Proc. nat. Acad. Sci., Wash.*, **27**, 145–9.

KLEINHOLZ, L. H. and HAVEL, V. J. (1948). The hyperglycemic effect of adrenalin injection in the crayfish, *Astacus trowbridgei. Anec. Rec.* **101**, 735.

KLEINHOLZ, L. H., HAVEL, V. J. and REICHART, R. (1950). Studies in the regulation of blood-sugar concentration in crustaceans. II. Experimental hyperglycemia and the regulatory mechanisms. *Biol. Bull., Woods Hole*, **99**, 454–68.

KLEINHOLZ, L. H. and KNOWLES, F. G. W. (1938). Studies in the pigmentary system of Crustacea. III. Light intensity and the position of the distal retinal pigment in *Leander adspersus. Biol. Bull., Woods Hole*, **75**, 266–73.

KLEINHOLZ, L. H. and LITTLE, B. C. (1948). Blood-sugar values in the marine crustacean *Libinia emarginata. Anat. Rec.* **101**, 734.

KLEINHOLZ, L. H. and LITTLE, B. C. (1949). Studies in the regulation of blood-sugar concentration in crustaceans. I. Normal values and experimental hyperglycemia in *Libinia emarginata. Biol. Bull., Woods Hole*, **96**, 218–27.

KLEINHOLZ, L. H. and WELSH, J. H. (1937). Colour changes in *Hippolyte varians. Nature, Lond.*, **140**, 851–2.

KNOWLES, F. G. W. (1939). The control of the white reflecting chromatophores in Crustacea. *Pubbl. Staz. zool. Napoli*, **42**, 174–82.

KNOWLES, F. G. W. (1940). Response of isolated white chromatophores of Crustacea to change of illumination. *Nature, Lond.*, **146**, 131.

KNOWLES, F. G. W. (1948). The problem of the number of hormones concerned in the pigment movements of crustaceans. *Bull. Biol.* Suppl. **33**, 149–59.

KNOWLES, F. G. W. (1949). Control of pigment migration in crustaceans. *Nature, Lond.*, **164**, 36.

KNOWLES, F. G. W. (1950). The control of retinal pigment migration in *Leander serratus. Biol. Bull., Woods Hole*, **98**, 66–80.

KNOWLES, F. G. W. (1951). Hormone production within the nervous system of a crustacean. *Nature, Lond.*, **167**, 564.

KNOWLES, F. G. W. (1952). Pigment movements after sinus-gland removal in *Leander adspersus. Physiol. comp.* **2**, 289–96.

KNOWLES, F. G. W. (1953*a*). Endocrine activity in the crustacean nervous system. *Proc. roy. Soc.* B, **141**, 248–67.

KNOWLES, F. G. W. (1953*b*). Neurosecretory pathways in the prawn *Leander serratus. Nature, Lond.*, **171**, 131.

KNOWLES, F. G. W. (1954). Neurosecretion in the tritocerebral complex of crustaceans. *Pubbl. Staz. zool. Napoli*, 24 Supp., 74–8.

KNOWLES, F. G. W. (1955). Crustacean colour change and neurosecretion. *Endeavour*, **14**, 95–104.

Knowles, F. G. W. (1956). Some problems in the study of colour change in crustaceans. *Ann. Sci. nat.* (*Zool.*), **18**, 315–24.

Knowles, F. G. W. and Callan, H. G. (1940). Change in the chromatophore pattern of Crustacea at sexual maturity. *J. exp. Biol.* **17**, 262–6.

Knowles, F. G. W. and Carlisle, D. B. (1956). Endocrine control in the Crustacea. *Biol. Rev.* **31**, 396–473.

Knowles, F. G. W., Carlisle, D. B. and Dupont-Raabe, M. (1955). Studies on pigment activating substances in animals. I. The separation by paper electrophoresis of chromactivating substances in arthropods. *J. mar. biol. Ass. U.K.* **34**, 611–35.

Knowles, F. G. W., Carlisle, D. B. and Dupont-Raabe, M. (1956). Inactivation enzymatique d'une substance chromactive des insectes et des crustacés. *C.R. Acad. Sci., Paris*, **242**, 825.

Koch, H. J. A. (1952). Eye stalk hormone, post moult volume increase and nitrogen metabolism in the crab *Eriocheir sinensis* (Milne Edwards). *Meded. vlaamsche Acad. Kl. Wet.* **14**, 3–11.

Koller, G. (1928). Versuche über die inkretorischen Vorgänge beim Garneelfarbwechsel. *Z. vergl. Physiol.* **8**, 601.

Koller, G. (1929). Die innere Sekretione bei wirbellosen Tieren. *Biol. Rev.* **4**, 269–306.

Koller, G. (1930). Weitere Untersuchungen über Farbwechsel und Farbwechselhormone bei *Crangon vulgaris*. *Z. vergl. Physiol.* **12**, 632–67.

Koller, G. (1938). *Hormone bei wirbellosen Tieren.* Leipzig.

Kropp, B. and Perkins, E. B. (1933). The occurrence of the humoral chromatophore activator among marine crustaceans. *Biol. Bull., Woods Hole*, **64**, 28–32.

Krøyer, H. (1842). Monographisk Fremstilling af slaegten *Hippolytes* nordiske arter. *K. danske vidensk. Selsk. Skr.* **9**, 209–361.

Kyer, D. L. (1942). The influence of the sinus glands on gastrolith formation in the crayfish. *Biol. Bull., Woods Hole*, **82**, 68–78.

Lattin, G. de and Gross, F. (1953). Die Beeinflussbarkeit sekundärer Geschlechtsmerkmale von *Oniscus asellus* durch die Gonaden. *Experientia*, **9**, 338–9.

Legrand, J.-J. (1954a). Induction des caractères sexuels secondaires mâles chez les femelles des Crustacés Isopodes terrestres par implantation testiculaire. *C.R. Acad. Sci., Paris*, **238**, 2030–2.

Legrand, J.-J. (1954b). Etude expérimentale de la différenciation du sexe chez les Crustacés Isopodes terrestres par implantation homoplastique et heteroplastique d'ovaires chez les mâles. *C.R. Acad. Sci., Paris*, **239**, 108–10.

Legrand, J.-J. (1954c). Effets de l'implantation d'un testicule chez les femelles des Crustacés Isopodes terrestres. *C.R. Acad. Sci., Paris*, **239**, 321–3.

Lenel, R. (1953a). Nature des pigments caroténoides de *Carcinus maenas* Pennant. *C.R. Acad. Sci., Paris*, **236**, 1090–2.

Lenel, R. (1953b). Localisation et métabolisme des pigments caroténoides chez *Carcinus maenas* Pennant. *C.R. Acad. Sci., Paris*, **236**, 1448–50.

Lerma, de B. (1936). L'attività endocrina negli invertebrati. *Att. Zool.* **2**, 83–135.

Lerma, de B., Dupont-Raabe, M. and Knowles, F. G. W. (1956). Sur la question de fluorescence des substances chromactives des Crustacés et des Insectes. *C.R. Acad. Sci.*, *Paris*, **241**, 995.

MATSUMOTO, K. (1954a). Chromatophorotropic activity of the neuro-secretory cells in the thoracic ganglion of *Eriocheir japonicus*. *Biol. J. Okayama Univ.* **1**, 234-8.

MATSUMOTO, K. (1954b). Neurosecretion in the thoracic ganglion of the crab, *Eriocheir japonicus*. *Biol. Bull.*, *Woods Hole*, **106**, 60-8.

MATSUMOTO, K. (1956). Migration of the neurosecretion products in the thoracic ganglion of the crab *Chionoectes opilio*. *Biol. J. Okayama Univ.* **2**, 137-46.

MATZDORFF, C. (1882/3). Ueber die Färbung von *Idotea tricuspidata* Desm. *Z. Naturw.* **16**, N.F. 9.

MENKE, H. (1911). Periodische Bewegungen und ihr Zusammenhang mit Licht und Stoffwechsel. *Pflug. Arch. ges. Physiol.* **140**, 37.

NAGANO, T. (1942). Physiological studies on the pigmentary system of Crustacea. I. The color change of a shrimp, *Paratya compressa* (de Haan). *Sci. Rep. Tohuku Univ.*, 4th Ser. (Biol.), **17**, 223-45.

NAGANO, T. (1949). Physiological studies on the pigmentary system of Crustacea. III. The color change of an isopod, *Ligia exotica* (Roux). *Sci. Rep. Tohuku Univ.*, 4th Ser. (Biol.), **18**, No. 2.

NAYAR, K. K. and PARAMESWARAN, R. (1955). Succinic dehydrogenase in the neurosecretory cells of the thoracic ganglion of the crab. *Curr. Sci.* **24**, 341.

NEEDHAM, A. E. (1954). Properties of minerals in the exuvia of Crustacea. *Quart. J. micr. Sci.* **95**, 183-90.

NEEDHAM, A. E. (1955). Nitrogen-excretion in *Carcinides maenas* (Pennant) during the early stages of regeneration. *J. Embryol. exp. Morph.* **3**, 189-212.

NEILAND, K. A. and SCHEER, B. T. (1953). The hormonal regulation of metabolism in crustaceans. V. The influence of fasting and of sinus gland removal on body composition of *Hemigrapsus nudus*. *Physiol. comp.* **4**, 321-6.

OKAY, S. (1945). Sur l'excitabilité directe des chromatophores, les changements périodiques de coloration et le centre chromatophorotropique chez *Sphaeroma serratum* Fabr. *Rev. Fac. Sci. Univ. Istanbul*, **9**B, 366-86.

ÖSTLUND, E. and EULER, U. S. VON (1957). Occurrence of substance P in the central nervous system of fish. *Rep. 2nd internat. Symp. Neurosecretion*, Springer-Verlag, Berlin.

ÖSTLUND, E. and FÄNGE, R. (1956). On the nature of the eyestalk hormone which causes concentration of red pigment in shrimps (Natantia). *Ann. Sci. nat.* (*Zool.*), **18**, 325-34.

PALAY, S. L. (1955). An electron microscope study of the neurohypophysis in normal, hydrated and dehydrated rats. *Anat. Rec.* **121**, 348.

PANOUSE, J. B. (1943). Influence de l'ablation du pédoncule oculaire sur la croissance de l'ovaire chez la crevette *Leander serratus*. *C.R. Acad. Sci.*, *Paris*, **217**, 553-5.

PANOUSE, J. B. (1944). L'action de la glande du sinus sur l'ovaire chez la crevette *Leander*. *C.R. Acad. Sci.*, *Paris*, **218**, 293-4.

PANOUSE, J. B. (1946). Recherches sur les phénomènes humoraux chez les

Crustacés. L'adaptation chromatique et la croissance ovarienne chez la Crevette *Leander serratus*. *Ann. Inst. océanogr.*, *Monaco*, **23**, 65–147.

PANOUSE, J. B. (1947). La glande du sinus et la maturation des produits génitaux chez les crevettes. *Bull. Biol.* (Suppl.), **33**, 160–3.

PANOUSE, J. B. (1947). Les correlations humorales chez les Crustacés. *Ann. biol.* **23**, 33–70.

PARAMESWARAN, R. (1955). Neurosecretory cells in *Paratelphusa hydrodromous* (Herbst). *Curr. Sci.* **24**, 23–4.

PARKER, G. H. (1897). Photochemical changes in the retinal pigment cells of *Palaemonetes*, and their relation to the central nervous system. *Bull. Mus. comp. Zool. Harv.* **30**, 275–300.

PASSANO, L. M. (1951 a). The X-organ sinus gland neurosecretory system in crabs. *Anat. Rec.* **III**, 502.

PASSANO, L. M. (1951 b). The X-organ, a neurosecretory gland controlling molting in crabs. *Anat. Rec.* **III**, 559.

PASSANO, L. M. (1952). Phase contrast observations on living neurosecretory cells of *Sesarma*. *Anat. Rec.* **112**, 460.

PASSANO, L. M. (1953). Neurosecretory control of molting in crabs by the X-organ sinus gland complex. *Physiol. comp.* **3**, 155–89.

PÉREZ-GONZÁLEZ, M. D. (1957). Evidence for hormone-containing granules in sinus glands of the Fiddler Crab *Uca pugilator*. *Biol. Bull.*, *Woods Hole*, **113**, 426.

PERKINS, E. B. (1928). Colour changes in crustaceans, especially in *Palaemonetes*. *J. exp. Zool.* **50**, 71–195.

PERKINS, E. B. and SNOOK, T. (1931). Control of pigment migration in the chromatophores of the crustaceans. *Proc. nat. Acad. Sci.*, *Wash.*, **17**, 282.

PIÉRON, H. (1914). Recherches sur le comportement chromatique des Invertébrés et en particulier des Isopodes. *Bull. Sci.*, *Fr. Belg.*, **48**, 30–79.

POLICE, G. (1908). Sul sistema nervosa viscerale dei Crostacei decapodi. *Mitt. zool. Sta. Neapel*, **19**, 69.

POTTER, D. D. (1954). Histology of the neurosecretory system of the blue crab *Callinectes sapidus*. *Anat. Rec.* **120**, 716.

POUCHET, G. (1872). Sur les rapides changements de coloration provoqués expérimentalement chez les Crustacés et sur les colorations bleues des poissons. *J. Anat.*, *Paris*, **8**, 401–7.

POUCHET, G. (1873). Recherches anatomiques sur la coloration bleue des Crustacés. *J. Anat.*, *Paris*, **9**, 290–307.

POUCHET, G. (1876). Des changements de coloration sous l'influence des nerfs. *J. Anat.*, *Paris*, **12**, 1–90, 113–65.

PYLE, R. W. (1943). The histogenesis and cyclic phenomena of the sinus gland and X-organ in Crustacea. *Biol. Bull.*, *Woods Hole*, **85**, 87–102.

ROBERTSON, J. D. (1957). New observations on the ultrastructure of the membranes of frog peripheral nerve fibers. *J. Biophysic. and Biochem. Cytol.* **3**, 1043–8.

RENAUD, L. (1949). Le cycle des réserves organiques chez les Crustacés Décapodes. *Ann. Inst. océanogr.*, *Monaco*, **24**, 259–357.

SANDEEN, M. I. (1950). Chromatophorotropins in the central nervous system of *Uca pugilator*, with special reference to their origins and actions. *Physiol. Zöol.* **23**, 337–52.

SANDEEN, M. I. and BROWN, F. A. (1952). Responses of the distal retinal pigment of *Palaemonetes* to illumination. *Physiol. Zoöl.* **25**, 222–30.

SAWAYA, P. (1939). Sobre a mudança da côr nos Crustaceos. *Bol. Fac. Fil., Ciên., Letr. Univ., S. Paolo,* **13**, 1–109.

SCHARRER, B. V. (1954). Neurosecretion in the invertebrates: a survey. *Pubbl. Staz. zool. Napoli,* 24, Suppl., 38–40..

SCHARRER, B. (1955). Hormones in invertebrates. *The Hormones,* **3,** 57–95. Academic Press, New York.

SCHARRER, E. (1954). Neurosecretion in the vertebrates: a survey. *Pubbl. Staz. zool. Napoli,* **24**, Suppl., 8–10.

SCHEER, B. T. and SCHEER, M. A. R. (1951). The hormonal regulation of metabolism in crustaceans. I. Blood sugar in spiny lobsters. *Physiol. comp.* **2**, 198–209.

SCHEER, B. T. and SCHEER, M. A. R. (1954*a*). The hormonal control of metabolism in Crustaceans. VII. Moulting and colour change in the prawn *Leander serratus. Pubbl. Staz. zool. Napoli,* **25**, 397–418.

SCHEER, B. T. and SCHEER, M. A. R. (1954*b*). The hormonal control of metabolism in Crustaceans. VIII. Oxygen consumption in *Leander serratus. Pubbl. Staz. zool. Napoli,* **25**, 419–26.

SCHEER, B. T., SCHWABE, C. W. and SCHEER, M. A. R. (1952). The hormonal regulation of metabolism in crustaceans. III. Tissue oxidation in crustaceans. *Physiol. comp.* **2**, 327–38.

SCHNEIDER, K. C. (1902). *Lehrbuch des vergleichenden Histologie.* Fischer, Jena.

SCUDAMORE, H. H. (1941). A correlation between the rate of heart beat and the state of certain chromatophores in the shrimp, *Palaemonetes. Trans. Ill. Acad. Sci.* **34,** 238.

SCUDAMORE, H. H. (1942). Hormonal regulation of molting and some related phenomena in the crayfish, *Cambarus immunis. Anat. Rec.* **84,** 514–15.

SCUDAMORE, H. H. (1947). The influence of the sinus glands upon molting and associated changes in the crayfish. *Physiol. Zool.* **20**, 187–208.

SJÖGREN, S. (1934). Die Blutdrüse und ihre Ausbildung bei den Decapoden. *Zool. Jb., Abt. Anat. Ontog. Tiere,* **58**, 145–70.

STÅHL, F. (1938*a*). Preliminary report on the colour changes and the incretory organs in the heads of some Crustaceans. *Ark. Zool.* **30** B, Nr. 8, 1.

STÅHL, F. (1938*b*). Über das Vorkommen von inkretorischen Organen und Farbwechselhormonen im Kopf einiger Crustaceen. *Kungl. Fysiogr. Sällsk. Handl.* **49**, Nr. 12, 1.

STEPHENS, G. C. (1952). The control of cement gland development in the crayfish, *Cambarus. Biol. Bull., Woods Hole,* **103**, 242–58.

STEPHENS, G. C. (1957). Twenty-four cycles in marine organisms. *Am. Nat.* **91**, 135.

STEPHENSON, E. M. (1934). Control of the chromatophores in *Leander serratus. Nature, Lond.,* **133**, 912.

SUNESON, S. (1947). Colour change and chromatophore activators in *Idothea. Lunds Univ. Asskr., N.F. Avd. 2,* **43**, 5. *Kungl. Fysiogr. Sällsk. Handl., N.F.,* **58**, 5.

TAKEWAKI, K. and NAKAMURA, N. (1944). The effects of gonadectomy on the sex characters of *Armadillidium vulgare,* an isopod crustacean. *J. Fac. Sci., Tokyo Univ.* (4), **6**, 369–82.

116

TEISSIER, G. (1935). Croissance des variants sexuels chez *Maia squinado* L. *Trav. Sta. biol., Roscoff*, **13**, 93–130.

THOMSEN, M. (1943). Effect of corpus cardiacum and other insect organs on the colour-change of the shrimp, *Leander adspersus*. *Biol. Medd., Kbh.* **19**, 1–38.

TRAVIS D. F. (1952a). The control of the sinus glands over certain aspects of calcium metabolism in *Panulirus argus* Latreille. *Anat. Rec.* **111**, 503.

TRAVIS, D. F. (1952b). Physiological changes which occur in the blood and urine of *Panulirus argus* Latreille during the molting cycle. *Anat. Rec.* **111**, 157.

TRAVIS, D. F. (1955). The moulting cycle of the spiny lobster, *Panulirus argus* Latreille. II. Pre-ecdysial histological and histo-chemical changes in the hepato-pancreas and integumental tissues. *Biol. Bull., Woods Hole*, **108**, 88–112.

TROJAN, E. (1913). Das Auge von *Palaemon squilla*. *Denksch. Kais. Akad. Wiss. Wien*, **88**, 291–344.

TURCHINI, J. (1953). Contribution à l'étude des organes X des Crustacés décapodes. *XIV. Intern. Zool. Congr., Copenhagen.*

VERNE, J. (1923). Essai histochimique sur les pigments tégumentaires des Crustacés décapodes. *Arch. Morph. gen. exp.* **16**, 1.

WALD, G., NATHANSON, N., JENCKS, W. P. and TARR, E. (1948). Crustacyanin, the blue carotenoid protein of the lobster shell. *Biol. Bull., Woods Hole*, **95**, 249.

WEBB, H. M., BENNETT, M. F. and BROWN, F. A. (1953). Persistence of an endogenous diurnal rhythmicity in eyestalkless *Uca pugilator*. *Anat. Rec.* **117**, 633–4.

WELSH, J. H. (1930a). The mechanics of migration of the distal pigment cells in the eyes of *Palaemonetes*. *J. exp. Zool.* **56**, 459–94.

WELSH, J. H. (1930b). Diurnal rhythm of the distal pigment cells in the eyes of certain crustaceans. *Proc. nat. Acad. Sci., Wash.*, **16**, 386–95.

WELSH, J. H. (1932). The nature and movement of the reflecting pigment in the eyes of crustaceans. *J. exp. Zool.* **62**, 173.

WELSH, J. H. (1937). The eyestalk hormone and rate of heart beat in Crustaceans. *Proc. nat. Acad. Sci.* **23**, No. 8, 458–60.

WELSH, J. H. (1939). The action of eyestalk extracts on retinal pigment migration in the crayfish, *Cambarus bartoni*. *Biol. Bull., Woods Hole*, **77**, 119–25.

WELSH, J. H. (1941). The sinus gland and 24-hour cycles of retinal pigment migration in the crayfish. *J. exp. Zool.* **86**, 35–49.

WINGSTRAND, K. G. (1954). Neurosecretion and antidiuretic activity in chick embryos with remarks on the subcommissural organ. *Ark. Zool.* **6**, 41–67.

INDEX

Figures in bold type indicate the pages on which the subject is most fully treated

premoult, **77**, 80
prepuberal moult, 79, 91
primary females, 93
proecdysis, **77**, 80, 81, 84, 86, 93
protandry, 93
proteins, 76, 89, 91
pterin, 42
puberty, 79

Queen bee substance, 101

Red pigment concentrator, 55
red pigment disperser, 55
Reptantia, 57, 98
respiratory metabolism, **91**
respiratory quotient, 76, 91
retinal pigment movements, **61**
rhabdome, 61
rhythms, 45, 86, 90

Sensory papilla, 33
sensory pore, 33
 X organ, 33, 82
Sesarma, 8, 36, 43
sex, **95**
sex reversal, **93**, 97, 99
sexual attractant, 93
sinus gland, 2, 8, **13**, 28, 39, 44, 52, 100
 and colour change, **46**
 and heart-beat, 74–5
 and moulting, 80
 and retinal pigments, 66
 and sex, 94, 98, 101
 and water balance, 85
Sphaeroma, 33
Squilla, 15, 27, 28, 29, 31, 39, 50, 70, 71, 74
steroid, 101
Stomatopoda, 25, 31, 35, 57, 71
stress, 87

substance A, **48**, 53, 57, 60, 61
substance A′, **50**, 56, **57**, 59, 61, 68
substance B, **51**, 54, **57**, 59, 61
substance P, 72
sugar, **87**
Systelaspis, 14

Temperature, 44
terminal anecdysis, 78–9, 91–3
testis, 97, 98, 101
thoracic ganglion, 36
tritocerebral commissure, 24, 47, 68

Uca, 2, 3, 5, 43, 44, 50, 52, 53, 54, 55, 78, 88
Uca-darkening substance, 3, 5, 52
Uca-red-dispersing substance, 54

Vas deferens, 79, 97, 98
vas deferens gland, 95
vitellogenesis, 99

Water balance, 10, **85**
water-balance regulating hormone, 82, **85**
Welsh X organ, 35
white pigment concentrator, 55, disperser, 55

X organ, 14, **33**
 and moulting, 81
 and sex, 94, 98
 and water balance, 85
X organ-sinus gland complex, **81**, 89, 92
X organ-sinus gland tract, 14–16, 20–21, 88
xanthophyll, 41

Y organ, **84**, 92–3, 95